Have You Tried This?

Have You Tried This?

THE ONLY SELF-CARE GUIDE YOU WILL EVER NEED

NICOLE GOODMAN &
LAUREN MISHCON

WELBECK
BALANCE

Published in 2024 by Welbeck Balance
An imprint of Welbeck Non-Fiction Limited
Part of Welbeck Publishing Group
Offices in: London – Carmelite House, 50 Victoria
Embankment, Temple, London EC4Y 0DZ &
Sydney – Level 17, 207 Kent St, Sydney NSW 2000 Australia
www.welbeckpublishing.com

Design and layout © Welbeck Non-Fiction Ltd 2024
Text © Lauren Mishcon & Nicole Goodman 2024

A CIP catalogue record for this book is available from the British Library.

ISBN
Hardback – 978-1-80129-313-6

Typeset by Lapiz Digital Services
Printed in Great Britain by Clays Ltd Elcograf S.p.A.

10 9 8 7 6 5 4 3 2 1

MIX
Paper from
responsible sources
FSC® C171272

Note/Disclaimer

Contents

Introduction

Welcome to yet another book on self-care. If you are expecting to read about how to run a bubble bath and where to buy Gwyneth's latest vagina-scented candle, then we've got news for you: that is not what this book is about, and it's not what self-care is – not even close.

The wellness industry is a multi-trillion-dollar industry, which promises to detox, nourish, replenish, awaken, strengthen, cleanse and resolve whatever needs fixing in our lives ... and often comes with a hefty price tag. It feels like every celeb is jumping on the wellness bandwagon, selling us something we never knew we needed.

But is spending £120 on a serum consisting of the mythical tears of Chios (yes, that is an actual ingredient in a celebrity product) really going to bring wellness to our lives? Or are these ongoing promises and expensive products just going to confuse and financially break us?

This book will show you that the most transformative and effective self-care practices cost nothing and take very little time out of your busy schedule. True wellness doesn't need to bankrupt you, and we are here to prove it.

MEET THE AUTHORS

Hi! We are Lauren and Nicole.

This book is inspired from our podcast *Self Care Club*. The premise of our show is to test out a different form of self-care every week, live it in real time and report back on the results – all in an effort to debunk the wellness world and bring true wellbeing and self-care back to people who need it now more than ever. Us included.

We met in September 2019 after guesting on each other's previous podcast and radio shows, and an unlikely friendship was born. Despite having absolutely nothing in common, we discovered we are the yin to each other's yang. It was platonic love at first sight.

We have both worked alongside women for decades: Lauren as a doula and Nicole as a women's coach and hairdresser; together, we are fiercely passionate about women's wellbeing.

But, unlike self-help "gurus", we rarely wear a kaftan (unless it's as a beach cover-up) and we make no claims to be experts in a world already overwhelmed by them. Our role is to offer peer-to-peer advice and guidance from our lived experience as very real women doing our best to function and stay (relatively) sane in a chaotic world.

As this book is very much based on our opinions and experiences, we thought we should tell you a bit more about ourselves.

Nicole

I'm 47 and live in north London with my husband and two daughters aged 15 and 13 (going on 25, hence why I need a lot of self-care) and my beautiful little Cavapoo, Miley. Did you say you wanted to see a pic?

I lead a very active lifestyle – I go to the gym five or six times a week and, outside of my friends and family, exercise is the most important element of my life. I cannot sit still. I've had a complicated relationship with exercise and food over the years, but as I move into my late 40s, being fit is so much more than just keeping myself trim – it's essential to my mental health; it helps me eat better, sleep better, stay mobile, and gives me more energy. Exercise seeps into every area of my life, and has given me some lifelong friends along the way.

I was a hairdresser for 30 years and ran my own salon. Six years ago, I became a certified life coach (I've even got some letters after my name), fell in love with coaching and began a small practice alongside my family life and salon. In August 2022, I retired from hairdressing, said goodbye to all my lovely clients, and moved into the coaching and podcasting space full time. I have never felt more complete in my professional life.

Lauren

I'm the youngster of our duo at just 46. I also live in north London with my husband, our three sons aged 20, 17 and 11 and my elderly but still sprightly Springer Spaniel, Barker. Unlike my podcasting pal, I do not go to the gym – I'm allergic. Whereas Nicole lives in her body, I tend to live more in my head. I am extremely happy to sit still reading a book; I'm a voracious reader and also a keen cook. If I'm not making food, then I'm thinking about it, watching a cooking show or listening to a podcast about it. I cook in silence and find it extremely meditative. If you're looking for me and I'm not in the kitchen then I'm in my local woods in a pair of red wellies walking Barker.

I trained as a birth doula after my second son was born and supported people through pregnancy and childbirth for 16 years. A doula (pronounced "doo-la") is an ancient Greek word meaning "woman servant"; it now refers to an experienced woman who offers emotional and practical support before, during and after childbirth. I am extremely grateful to have been in attendance at around 200 births. I have seen everything from home deliveries through to waterbirths and caesareans; in seven cases I had to deliver the babies myself when they decided to arrive in great haste. Bearing witness to the everyday miracle of life is an honour, and being invited to support people at such a vulnerable and special time in their life is a great privilege. My job has made me comfortable with every bodily fluid, impossible to embarrass and a big fan of the amazing vagina.

THE BIRTH OF *SELF CARE CLUB*

The initial idea for *Self Care Club* was formed over coffee, when, during a mutual rant, we realised that self-care had become yet another burden to add on to women's mental load.

In today's world, we are faced with the stress and pressure of building a career, keeping a perfect home, raising impeccably behaved children, keeping up with friendships, navigating school WhatsApp groups, having amazing sex with our partner 800 times a week, looking like we've never had a baby (even if you've had three), dressing in the latest trends, never being allowed to age (colouring grey hairs, filling any wrinkles) and making this all look effortless. We are also bombarded on an hourly basis via advertising and social media with products that promise to fix a problem that we didn't even know we had, which makes us feel crap and insecure. As if we are not already doing enough (and even when we are, we're probably doing it wrong), self-care has become another huge and impossible job.

In order to help lighten the load for other women, we decided – for better or worse – to sacrifice ourselves at the altar of self-care for the greater good. In an industry that makes a lot of promises for a lot of money, we felt it our duty to debunk it all. Call it a national service, if you will.

TRY, TRY AND TRY AGAIN

Since starting *Self Care Club* in 2020, we have acted as human guinea pigs, immersing ourselves in the wellness game and testing out hundreds of self-care practices. Every product you can imagine, every fad that has hit the scene – we have tried it.

Floating in an enclosed pod filled with saltwater for an hour in the pitch black? We've tried it.

Standing in just our underwear in a chamber frozen to -125°C? We've tried that too.

Cold showers? Tick.

Yoga with goats? How about with puppies? We have done both. Verdict: not much yoga, a lot of animal poop.

Napping in a salt cave? Been there, done it.

Rolling our face with crystals to help wrinkles and having a healer come and place them all over our bodies to balance our chakras? Yep.

Sticking CBD up our ... no, not up there, but CBD tampons *are* a thing and, well, let's just leave that there.

We've steamed, exfoliated, scrubbed, breathed, slept, run, rested, juiced, whitened, heated, frozen, cuddled (trees and strangers), sweated, lasered, drunk, laughed and sung in search of the true meaning of self-care.

Here's what we learnt: the easiest, most cost-effective ways of truly looking after your emotional, mental and physical needs don't include a toxic vampire spray that cleanses your aura (yep, we tried that too); but they *do* include things like learning the art of how to say "no", how to stop people pleasing, how to receive a compliment, and how to ask for what you want. These are life skills that can transform your relationship with others and with yourself.

What we have also discovered on our exploration is that self-care isn't complicated, expensive or elusive. It is simply about taking care of the most important person in your life: You.

Self-care is accessible and available to all, regardless of your age, sex, race, class or social status. It is about far more than finding the perfect serum or drinking the latest wellness tea; it's about pausing and figuring out what it is you need on that particular day or in that specific moment, and about finding those small tweaks that truly improve your wellbeing and your life so you can live in a way that makes you feel fulfilled, happy and content.

The most important thing is that it must be self-care that suits *you*. For some, this might be a need to put boundaries in place; for others, it may be finding a way to move your body that you enjoy (Lauren is still waiting to discover this). Whether it's internal or external work you need assistance with, we are here to help.

(Side note: If you have managed to find the perfect serum then please DM us; but if it contains mythical tears of whatever, don't bother!)

WHY WE WROTE THIS BOOK

You don't need to know our podcast to read this book. Whether you've been with us from the start (thank you!) or you've only just found us now (hello!), either way we are delighted that you're here. Maybe you've had it gifted to you by somebody in your life who cares about you, or maybe you've picked it up and are browsing this introduction debating whether to buy it (the answer is yes, you'll love it). Here, we have gathered everything we have tried on the show into one place and put it to paper, along with some brand-new, exclusive practices and experiences we tried just for the book.

Each practice in this book has been thoroughly tested by both of us and has gone through a rigorous process to ensure it really does improve your wellbeing. We hope you take comfort in knowing that whatever you are tempted to step into we have already done it and in all but one occasion recommend it.

Please also know that every single practice we recommend in this book will not cost you a penny. We believe true self-care should not take anything *away* from you – not money, time or your mental health – it is there purely to *add* to your life and enrich it.

This really is your ultimate guide to self-care. Think of it as a one-stop shop to wellness without the bullshit.

Each chapter tackles a different familiar struggle that we all face at one time or another, and gives step-by-step instructions on how to integrate appropriate self-care practices for that issue into your everyday life. For clarity and transparency, we share our own experiences of the practices; some of these are funny, some are profound, and all of them are deeply personal and honest. We are not doctors or health professionals, and all the advice in this book comes from our hearts and lived experience. Further resources are available at the back of the book for more support.

We hope this book will empower you to find pleasure and curiosity in taking care of yourself. Welcome to the club!

WHAT IS SELF-CARE?

Self-care is simply the act of taking care of yourself. Self-care consists of mental, physical, emotional and spiritual practices that improve your life and enable you to thrive in the world by making you smile, lifting you up, bringing you joy and helping you feel great.

Beauty treatments and pampering have their place and can be a lovely way to nurture yourself, but they also have their limits when it comes to the results. As such, we call them "plaster practices". Let's dig a little deeper.

PLASTER PRACTICES

Plaster practices is our name for short-term fixes to long-term problems. Yes, a relaxing bath will soothe a difficult day at the office, but it will not help you deal with your burnout or teach you how to have a difficult conversation with your boss. The stress cycle will simply continue.

Plaster practices are enjoyable (which is why we do them), and they play a small, sweet role in the self-care journey. But, just like bad romantic partners, they tend to have a short lifespan – they feel good in the moment, but they won't fix what's truly going on underneath the surface.

Using the practices in this book, we will get to the root of the larger issues together and bring longevity to your overall wellbeing. The work may feel hard at times, and it may take longer than you would like to get to where you want to be, but rest assured the rewards will be worth it.

We will gently guide you into finding what works best and help you avoid any of the pitfalls and mistakes that we made along the way – and, believe us, we made many; all of which we share with you in the spirit of camaraderie and, in some cases, just to give you a good laugh.

EXCUSES

Before we jump into the good stuff, we should probably take a moment to chat about what may be stopping you from practising self-care.

Do any of the following statements sound familiar to you?

I don't have time
I have too much to do
I don't know where to start
I can't afford it
There's too much choice
I don't know what works
I feel guilty taking time for myself
It's self-indulgent
Self-care is selfish
I don't want to clutter my house with more "stuff"
I'm embarrassed
I feel self-conscious
I'm too old
I'm too young
I'm too overweight
I'm too unfit
I'm fine as I am
I don't trust the wellness world

These are the common excuses we've heard and even used ourselves, time and time again. Excuses keep you in the same place – they prevent growth and change because they make rational, valid arguments against the thing that you really want to achieve. If you continue to make excuses, you will stay where you are. It's as simple and harsh as that. Sorry (not sorry).

Let's take the excuse of "I can't afford it". This is often a genuine excuse; but if you keep telling yourself, "I can't afford to look after myself", that narrative keeps you in a place where you are not able to practise self-care. It becomes a truth and then a behaviour, which keeps you from action.

LOOK FOR THE POSSIBILITY

While you may not be able to afford a fancy gym membership or a massage at a hotel spa, there are many other ways of engaging in something kind and nourishing for yourself. Just look for the possibility and you will find it. For example, you can go for a daily walk, meditate, reach out to a friend, or start the Couch to 5k running programme.

> **Lauren:** *Oh this again. Stop with the Couch to 5K; I refuse to do the Couch to 5K.*
> **Nicole:** *I'm not suggesting you do the Couch to 5K. No one wants to live through that again. Most of all, me.*

Try not to focus on the excuse, which in this instance is "I can't afford it", and focus on the possibility/solution: "What can I do that will benefit me, but costs nothing?"

So, take a look at that list of excuses again. Are they true, or are they just another reason to stop you from helping yourself? They might *feel* true – after all, few people have free hours or spare cash to dedicate to self-care. But put the excuses aside for a moment and ask yourself, "What is it that I want?"

If you want to make changes, you can. The choice is yours. We invite you to choose yourself and your wellbeing.

MAKING TIME

Everyone has the same 24 hours in a day. (Although we believe that one third of those hours should actually be spent getting decent, restful sleep.) Some people manage to fit in a run, their chores, breakfast and a dog walk all before starting work; those people are quite annoying, and Nicole is one of them. Others wait until the very last minute to get out of bed and then rush out the house with a coffee in their hand – Lauren, we're looking at you.

The important point is: this is not about *having* the time, it's about *making* the time. Choosing to make the time is what's going to bring more self-care into your space.

You may be reading this thinking, "I don't have these magical extra hours of spare time", and you would be right. But what you *do* have is the ability to switch your focus. Carving out a space in the week to introduce something helpful and positive is time well spent. It's not time wasted, taking you away from something else; it's adding an element of richness. It may also mean that you no longer waste hours doing things that don't serve you well, such as mindlessly scrolling through social media. Instead, you could be going for a walk in nature or sitting down and taking five deep breaths.

Our suggested practices won't set you back financially, but you *will* have to carve out the moments to do them. But that's all part of the discipline of making yourself a priority. And, by the way, it's not arduous – it's actually fun. Pinky swear.

HOW TO USE THIS BOOK

We want this book to be a collaborative experience, where you are not just a passive reader but a person becoming accountable for their own self-care.

To help you understand where you currently sit in all areas of your self-care, we begin the book with a Wellness Wheel. The wheel is divided into eight segments that reflect the chapters of the book. It's a bit like a pie in Trivial Pursuit but you don't need to know which country displays the Vitruvian Man on one of its coins in order to gain a blue pie.* Once you have answered the questions and filled in your initial score (see page 19), you will have a visual representation of where your self-care gaps sit. Wherever you score low, you can jump straight to that chapter to learn how to improve your self-care in that area.

For example, if your anxiety scores at an all-time high, start with the Calm chapter and then move towards whichever chapters call to you. This book is for you, so read it in a way that works for you – there are no rules here.

Each chapter offers two or three different practices that we personally tested out. The practices become increasingly more challenging as the chapter progresses.

For each practice, we lay out its benefits, a step-by-step guide as to how to do it yourself, and then we will tell you with brutal honesty how we got on when we tried it out.

There were certain non-negotiables when we decided on what practices to include.

---

* The answer is Italy

- It had to be completely free of charge
- We had to be willing to try it out ourselves
- It had to bring a tangible benefit to your life and wellbeing

At the end of every chapter, you will find takeaway tips and challenges to help cement the ideas and bring the practices into your life in a practical and manageable way. We want you to not only read and enjoy this book, but to begin using the practices to enhance your own life and wellbeing.

At the end of the book, you will revisit the Wellness Wheel; by completing it again, you will be able to see how far you have come and compare your scores from the start of the book to the end. It is a lovely opportunity to see the learning in action in your own life.

The Wellness Wheel

Behold! Welcome to the Wellness Wheel.

Every section of the wheel tallies up with a chapter in the book.

If we were to ask you right now, "How are you?", you might struggle to answer as it's a very big question. Some areas of your life may be thriving, while other areas might need attention and improvement.

So, before reading on, we would encourage you to take five minutes to fill in your Wellness Wheel. This is going to help you understand where you are currently when it comes to different areas of your self-care, and show you what you may want to focus on or improve. After filling in the wheel it will be immediately obvious what areas need attention and where you are thriving.

WELLNESS QUESTIONS

First off, ask yourself the questions below relating to each segment of the wheel. Decide on a score between 1 and 10 that you feel correlates best to you, with 1 being where your self-care is depleted in this area of your life and 10 being where you have it licked.

Then, fill in each section on the blank wheel on page 19 with these scores.

BOUNDARIES

How good are you at respecting your own boundaries?

1: Just call me (door)Mat because I let everyone walk all over me.

10: It's easier to get into a high-security prison than to cross my boundary.

Fill in your score on the wheel.

SELF-LOVE

How much love do you have for yourself?

1: I can't find one nice thing to say about myself.

10: I'm fabulous darling.

Fill in your score on the wheel.

CONFIDENCE

How confident are you?

1: I'm scared to look people in the eye.

10: Put me in any room and I will work it.

Fill in your score on the wheel.

CALM

How calm do you feel in mind and body?

1: Chaos is my middle name. I live on adrenalin and coffee.

10: Namaste.

Fill in your score on the wheel.

BODY IMAGE

When you look in the mirror, do you like what you see?

1: I try not to look unless I absolutely have to.

10: Hello, you gorgeous bitch!

Fill in your score on the wheel.

PHYSICAL HEALTH

How active are you?

1: I could put a sloth to shame. (Lauren)

10: Can't talk, in the gym. (Nicole)

Fill in your score on the wheel.

RELATIONSHIPS

How healthy are your relationships?

1: My healthiest relationship is with the Deliveroo driver.

10: My relationships are supportive, loving, understanding and mutually respectful.

Fill in your score on the wheel.

WORK–LIFE BALANCE

How is your work–life balance?

1: I've scheduled a Zoom call with my kids Thursday week (remind me their names again).

10: Working 9 to 5 (what a way to make a living – just call me Dolly Parton) then I come home and switch off.

Fill in your score on the wheel.

OUR WHEELS

In the spirit of transparency, here are our current wheels.

Lauren's wheel

Nicole's wheel

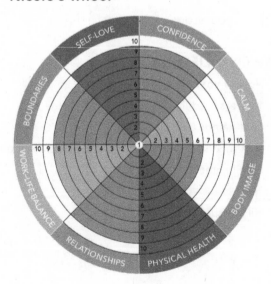

YOUR WELLNESS WHEEL

Fill in your scores from the questions on pages 16 and 17 on the below wheel.

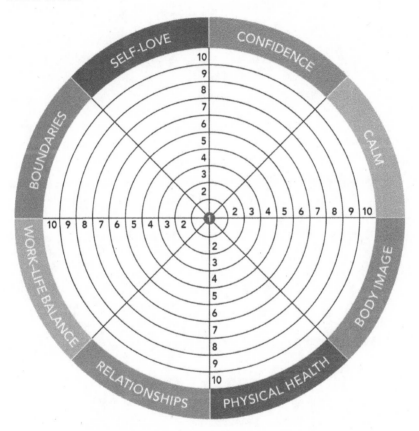

At the end of the book, we invite you to come back to the Wellness Wheel and answer the questions again. Compare your wheel above with the wheel with your new scores on page 226 to see the improvements you have made.

1

Boundaries

We believe that boundaries are the epitome of self-care, so consider this as the flagship chapter of the book. We are going to explore:

- What boundaries are
- Why boundaries are so imperative to our wellbeing
- How to use boundaries to improve every relationship we have – especially our relationship with ourselves.

The practices in this chapter will hopefully seep into every aspect of your life and help to create an empowered relationship with yourself. You will be able to come back to this chapter to be guided by the tools whenever you feel out of alignment with yourself or a situation.

So, with that big promise in mind, let's begin at the very beginning by defining what a boundary is.

WHAT IS A BOUNDARY?

According to Nancy Levin, author, coach and the queen of boundary work, boundaries are "the limits that we set around what we will or will not do, will or will not tolerate or will or will not accept".

WHY ARE BOUNDARIES IMPORTANT?

Boundaries are vital to our sense of self as they give us an awareness of what we want and don't want in our lives. They help us establish and maintain a healthy sense of identity, autonomy and self-respect while protecting our wellbeing, values and personal space.

HOW TO USE BOUNDARIES IN DIFFERENT RELATIONSHIPS

There are seven different types of boundaries.

1. **Emotional** boundaries protect your right to have your own feelings and to not have them criticised or invalidated by other people. You are not responsible for how other people feel.
2. **Physical** boundaries protect your space and body and determine when you allow physical touch.
3. **Mental** boundaries keep you in touch with what you think. You always have the right to your own thoughts and opinions.
4. **Social** boundaries protect you from engaging in social activities that you don't want to attend and help you prioritise the ones that you do.
5. **Financial** boundaries help you to manage your finances and not overspend where you can't afford to.
6. **Spiritual** boundaries are about believing in whatever you wish to and standing by those spiritual beliefs.
7. **Sexual** boundaries protect your right to consent and to ask for what you like and don't like sexually.

BENEFITS OF BOUNDARIES

Setting boundaries is full of benefits and possibilities. Among other things, establishing a boundary:

- Improves your relationship with yourself
- Improves your relationship with others

- Builds self-confidence
- Gives you the ability to live life on your own terms
- Blocks what you *don't* want
- Creates more of what you *do* want
- Brings you more energy
- Builds self-esteem
- Allows you to be more authentic
- Reduces stress and anxiety

So if they are so beneficial, why don't we set boundaries more often?

One reason we may not feel comfortable setting a boundary arises when we are overly tuned in to what others think, prioritising other people's wants and needs above our own. The thought of putting boundaries in place can be an issue if you are overly concerned with others' experiences – AKA you're a people-pleaser. Wanting to be liked becomes more important than our wants and needs, and we subconsciously believe that if we do what others want then they will love and accept us.

Another reason we might not set a boundary is because we may be conflict-avoidant, and putting a boundary in place can activate our fear of upsetting someone. We also often believe that if we set a boundary, it will inconvenience and potentially annoy someone. More often than not, this private narrative is built on a made-up assumption that we haven't bothered to share with the other person, and in turn makes us behave in an unintentionally disingenuous way.

THE PRACTICES

For this chapter, we chose the practices that we felt do justice to this important work.

- **Setting boundaries**
- **How to say "no"**
- **How to stop people-pleasing**

SETTING BOUNDARIES

Many women are conditioned to think of everyone else first and themselves last. Whether that's our self-care, our emotional needs or something as simple as what we want to eat for dinner, we often prioritise others before we ask, "What do I want?". We disown our needs to such a degree that selflessness becomes a badge of honour. This mindset leads to us losing sight of our own needs and allows people, habits, situations and behaviours into our lives that drain our energy, and we run the risk of disappearing. Boundaries are the solution to all of this, and setting them will add to your life in ways you never thought possible.

Boundaries are not a restriction or a restraint; you can choose to experience them as expansive. They give you the ability to carefully curate the content of your own life. When you have clear, healthy boundaries that you set and hold and take responsibility for, then freedom is limitless. You can move away from the role of "victim" and blaming others for the issues in your life and move into a responsible, empowered place creating the life that you want to live in the way you want to live it. You have a lot to gain from setting boundaries.

BOUNDARY EXAMPLE

A friend who you haven't seen for ages wants to go for an early dinner, but you are on a huge work deadline. You immediately feel guilty for saying no to the dinner because you haven't seen them for ages. So, you put the deadline (i.e. your needs) to the side and let your guilt lead the way. You go for dinner but sit there stressed and resentful because you know you should have prioritised your work. Perhaps you mentally blame your friend for "making you" go to the dinner, but the truth is, you simply needed to set a boundary the moment they asked. You could have said something like:

> *"I would love to go for dinner with you as we haven't seen one another for a while, but I have a deadline. Please can we arrange something for a few weeks when I have caught up with my work?"*

Sound familiar?

Unfun Fact

When you don't set a boundary, the person you are upset with is yourself.

It's harsh, we know, but read it again until it sinks in because it's immensely important.

Let's separate two crucial elements here: 1) your boundary and 2) how someone reacts to it.

You are not responsible for how people respond to your boundaries. You also don't need anyone else's approval on your boundaries. You are allowed to set boundaries, regardless of how others interpret it – and how others choose to react is their choice. As Nancy Levin explains: "It's not our responsibility to manage anyone else's response to our truth." You can only be responsible for yourself and for what you allow and don't allow in your life.

The uncomfortable fact is that it's up to you to set and hold your boundaries. It's not anyone else's job but yours. If you find your boundaries are being crossed, then *you* are the one crossing them.

> **Lauren:** *Wow, it sounds quite brutal when it's set out like that.*
> **Nicole:** *Yes, it's rough, but brilliant at the same time. The beauty is that you always have the agency to set a boundary and limit what isn't working for you, and empower more of what will. This work enables you to always be in control of your own life, rather than blaming someone or something else. That blame only ever keeps you stuck. Knowing this is transformative.*

Boundary work is one of the hardest parts of self-love. The trick is to make peace with the fact that you may upset others, but living by other people's standards and ideals will leave you exhausted and drained.

Your boundaries are yours and yours alone, even if they involve another person. They are there so you can live your life in a way that works for you! If it's inconvenient to someone else, that's simply not your burden to carry.

SELF-CARE STEPS FOR SETTING BOUNDARIES

Step 1: The pause
When someone asks or expects something of you, remember you are not obliged to answer immediately. Create a moment of pause and ask yourself:

- *What do I think, what do I feel, what do I need?*
- *Do I have the energy needed for this?*
- *Do I have time for this?*
- *Is this something I want?*

Step 2: Define where a boundary may be needed

Everyone's boundaries are personal to them. But one way to identify your boundaries is to think about the areas of your life where you're experiencing problems. Do you constantly feel exhausted? Do you feel resentful of your mother's intrusions? Do you feel you are never being heard by one of your close friends? Each of these problems is a sign that you're lacking boundaries in this area of your life.

Step 3: Define what boundary needs to be set

Now you have established where a boundary is needed in your life, ask yourself: *What would help me feel better in this situation?*

Take the example of dinner with a friend; if you check in with yourself first (creating a pause), you would know that you need to prioritise work and therefore won't end up resentfully sitting at a table.

Step 4: Set the boundary

Communicate assertively: clearly and directly communicate your boundaries to others. You do not need to give ultimatums. Keep the conversation focused on using "I" statements to express how *you* feel and what *you* need. For example, say, "I feel overwhelmed when I have too many commitments, so I need to prioritise my time right now."

Step 5: Set it with love and kindness

Boundaries are an act of kindness both to yourself and the other person. Setting a boundary is uncomfortable, but it can always be done with love. Be assertive and express your needs without being aggressive or passive.

OUR EXPERIENCE

Lauren

I am better at setting and keeping work boundaries than personal ones. In my personal life I will allow myself to be manipulated, and it's only when I finally get to the end of my long rope that I will be cornered into implementing a boundary. The fear of being "selfish" is a big thing with me, and often I would rather overstep my own boundary and feel resentful than be perceived as selfish or have to step into potential conflict. I knew this would be a good practice for me and would serve me well, despite being hard.

My practice began with an email enquiry from a potential doula client. We agreed to an initial phone call. As soon as we got on the call, she immediately asked if we could switch to Facetime. In the most minute way, she had just crossed my boundary. I should have said no, but I didn't, because it felt petty. I had never met this woman and I didn't want the first thing I said to her to be "no". I felt pushed into something we hadn't agreed on and worried about how she would perceive me if I had refused, even though I had been taught that I am not responsible for how anyone responds to my boundary.

During the Facetime call, a load of red flags came up for me. The very first thing she wanted to discuss was what constituted a refund. "Would you refund me if X happens? What about if Y happens?" She didn't want to ask anything about how I work, my ethos or my experience, which is a little unusual when you are looking to hire a birth partner. She then said that she wanted to book me on the spot. I said that wasn't possible as my doula partner, Nina, was away, and this woman's partner was also not on the call. I explained that everyone involved needed to meet to make sure it was a good fit for us all. This led to her having a neurotic panic that if we waited a week then I would get booked by someone else, followed by ten minutes more of asking me what else I offered on top of all the services I had already explained. I told her we would speak again when my doula partner returned and that I would not be taking on anyone else in the meantime.

I soon realised that nothing was ever going to be enough for her; whatever I provided, she would always want more. That evening I got a text message from her. "I want you to commit to being my doula and during the labour I want it to be you who is there not Nina and want you to commit to that now." I reiterated that who attended the birth would depend on the day and time she was in labour. I also reminded her that she had not met Nina and may, in fact, like her far more than me! I put a pause in place and said I would get back to her in a few days. I spoke to Nina about my concerns. We weighed up the mental and physical energy this woman and this job would take, and felt instinctively that it would be wrong to take her on when I was already feeling uncomfortable.

I woke up a few days later suddenly ready to set the boundary. I sent a text saying that, unfortunately, I would not be able to support her but we wished her all the best for a positive and empowering birth experience. No apology or excuses, just a boundary that was set with kindness. I had a feeling that there would be backlash, and was not surprised to receive the following reply: "I'm really disappointed, I feel really upset, I was looking forward to working with you. Can you juggle this? Can you change that? Can you accommodate me?" I read it through and realised that I didn't feel I was required to cross my boundary, change my mind, explain myself or be emotionally manipulated by someone I don't owe anything to. There was nothing that warranted a reply, so I chose not to.

Nicole

In June 2022, I found myself sitting in Fenwick's furniture department having a panic attack. I had woken up feeling a tightness in my chest and the sense that I could burst into tears at any moment. Looking back, I had been feeling this way for months.

I ran a private hair salon and had been hairdressing for 29 years; it was so second nature to me it was like brushing my teeth. Over the years, I had built myself a brilliant reputation and a thriving business. I was completely in love with hairdressing until I turned 40, when I began to feel restless and needed something else. I trained for two years to become a certified coach, set up a small practice and, shortly after, started the podcast.

Multi-tasking all three roles was causing a lot of anxiety and had become unmanageable. Every time a client arrived, I needed to take a deep breath. I dreaded my "hairdressing" days. The podcast was in full swing: we were releasing three shows a week, our numbers were great and Lauren and I were producing every part of it. I knew I wanted to go full time into the podcast, but the money I was earning in the salon always stopped me; I kept telling myself it was "easy" money.

As I found myself struggling to breathe while sitting on a very expensive couch, I realised there was nothing "easy" about it anymore. I was living in a constant state of overwhelm.

There had been many signs that I wasn't coping, but I had ignored them. This panic attack was the catalyst I needed to put a boundary in place, let go of what was draining me and move myself towards what was fulfilling me.

It was the biggest decision I have ever made. I chose an end date that was two months away, making sure every client had one last haircut. The last few weeks in my salon were very special, filled with tears, hugs and lots of good wishes. I still miss some of my lovely clients, but I have never missed doing anyone's hair, not even for a millisecond.

WHAT DID WE LEARN?

Lauren

Setting boundaries allowed me to conserve physical, emotional and mental energy and reduced my mental load. It gave me agency to put myself first and centre, which isn't my default setting but was necessary. I couldn't give this woman what she needed – my heart and good intent – which would not have been fair on her or on me. I know that if I am feeling resentment then it's on me to implement a boundary. I need to look a little harder at using my time well and use it to serve myself as well as others. Any resentment that I may feel around that is my own responsibility, and it's my choice to either accept it with grace or place a boundary around it and change.

Nicole

Boundaries are the most important part of self-preservation and self-love. Setting one may be filled with discomfort and difficulty, but that is not an indicator that you shouldn't.

Through this practice, I really learnt to listen to my body. It was tired, stressed and anxious anytime I was around hairdressing or even talking about it. I think we ignore the warning signs as they are always inconvenient; but ignoring them doesn't make them go away, it just means they have to scream louder.

HOW TO SAY "NO"

When someone asks you for a favour or invites you to an event, do you find yourself immediately saying, "Sounds great!" or, "I'd love to!", before you have even mentally processed the request? If so, you are certainly not alone! We have internalised the message that being a good friend/partner/employee/parent/human means always saying yes.

The word "no" is underutilised in society. Women, in particular, are still expected from a young age to be agreeable and go with the flow. Studies show that saying "no" is more challenging for women because of societal pressures to be likeable. Men are still seen as likeable if they're assertive, while women are more likely to be seen as likeable if they're compliant.

Most of the time, not being able to implement the "no" in our life lies in unconscious habits or beliefs. We fear confrontation, or we don't want to seem selfish, or we worry that saying "no" will hurt someone's feelings or disappoint them. Not only is this focus all wrong, this is classic societal conditioning: we wrongly assume that saying "no" may equate to an argument or cause an unpleasant situation.

We are here to break that assumption and bring the focus back to you and your needs.

Focusing on how the other person will react, rather than on the wonderful benefits that come with saying "no" to things that don't serve us, puts us at risk of fostering resentment, stress, mental exhaustion and general depletion. This section is going to open you up to things you *actually* want to say "yes" to. It's a powerful shift and a life-changing practice. Saying "no" is – like boundaries – a fundamental part of our self-care.

BENEFITS OF SAYING "NO"
Saying "no":

- Ensures we only commit to things we really want to
- Creates more trusting relationships
- Creates more self-love and self-trust
- Creates more confidence and self-belief
- Allows us to live with integrity
- Frees us from making shallow and insincere commitments
- Leaves space for us to say "yes" to the things we want for ourselves

Before we jump in, keep in mind saying "no" takes practice. You wouldn't walk into a gym for the first time and expect to pick up a very heavy weight and lift it ...

Lauren: Well Nicole would.

It takes practice; saying "no" is the same.

SELF-CARE STEPS TO SAYING "NO"

Step 1: Focus on your YES

When you say "no" to something, realise that you are really saying "yes" to something else; focusing on that yes will ease the discomfort of the no.

For example: A friend asks you to go to an event with them on Friday night. You don't want to go as you want to get up early the next morning, not be hungover and go to a yoga class. Your "yes" is to yoga, so your focus starts there and you politely decline: "Thank you, but I'm going to say no as I'm doing an early yoga class tomorrow."

Step 2: It's okay to put your own needs first

Give yourself permission to prioritise yourself, and remind yourself that your needs are just as important as someone else's.

Step 3: Tell the truth

Lying will lead to guilt and anxiety, which is exactly what you're trying to avoid. Say "no" from a place of truth and love.

Step 4: Say "no" to the request, not the person

Remember that you're not rejecting the person, just declining their invitation. Kindness and respect go a long way here.

For example: *"I am going to say 'no' to the event, but thank you so much for the invite."*

Step 5: Be appreciative

It's not an insult when people make requests of you. Thank them for thinking of you or making the request/invitation AND THEN POLITELY DECLINE.

OUR EXPERIENCE

Lauren

I often find it difficult to say "no". It's ingrained in who I am as a woman and my conditioning. I am the eldest child, I am conformist and I am averse to confrontation. I have historically said "yes" to many things that I knew I didn't want to do and were actually detrimental to me, but I sucked them up and consequently felt resentful.

The practice began when I was going on a trip with my youngest son, my sister-in-law, Eliza, and my niece. The journey involved motorway driving for a couple of hours and my car was the only one that could fit us all in. I desperately didn't want to drive as I have become fearful of motorway driving since Covid-19, when I didn't drive anywhere for a long time. However, my instinct was to automatically say "yes". I didn't want to cause a fuss, as refusing to drive would have meant that alternative arrangements would need to be made. I knew that Eliza would have been very accommodating and understanding of my reasons, so this was purely about me feeling embarrassed about saying "no" and feeling uncomfortable at perhaps being thought of as "difficult" or as a burden.

Nevertheless, I had an internal struggle knowing that if I said "yes", I was going to have a week beforehand of worrying and anxiety, when I could just say "no" and be immediately relaxed. Eliza and I settled on a "suck it and see" approach, with the option of me not having to do it if I felt I couldn't. I was made to feel very safe in that I wasn't letting her down and she understood my reasoning.

I would call this a "weak no", as I did feel an endless need to justify it. On the day of the trip, I was encouraged by my husband, and decided that it would be beneficial to me to confront my fears head on and do the drive. I tackled three motorways and a thunderstorm and we all got there unscathed. I was proud of and amazed at myself. The next day, the realisation of having to drive home dawned on me, and I baulked. My anxiety grew. I had to put myself first and be honest about how I was feeling. I said that the previous day's journey had pushed me to my limit and I didn't feel okay about driving home. My sister-in-law immediately understood. She very kindly insured herself on my car and did the return journey with no hesitation and without shaming me or making me feel embarrassed.

Nicole

Going into this practice I felt that on the whole I am good with "no"; I have used it over the years many times due to the nature of my career in hairdressing. I learnt from an early age that "no" had to be a solid part of my self-care, otherwise I would have burnt out trying to please 300 clients.

One time that springs to mind was when a new client was becoming very unreliable. I ran a tight ship in my salon – if you had a 3pm appointment, then you were seen at 3pm. Time is very important to me as it's a very limited resource for all of us, so it needs to be used wisely.

This woman quickly made her way onto my "late list". (Late list clients were told their appointments were 15 minutes before they were actually scheduled for.)

For the first appointment she had turned up 15 minutes late; 15 minutes to a hairdresser is the difference between a lovely day and a very stressful one. It meant I ran late for everyone who came after her. I let it go as she was a new client. I politely explained how my salon ran and if she was more than 10 minutes late again, I sadly wouldn't be able to accommodate her. She apologised and said she understood.

The next time, she arrived late again. The third time, she booked for a two-hour appointment. She didn't turn up, so after 20 minutes I called to see where she was. She said she was on her way and would be there in 20 minutes. I informed her I couldn't do her hair as she would be too late. I was furious.

She turned up at the salon one hour after her time slot and proceeded to beg me to do her hair. It was awful. I said, "This isn't going to work. I'm a very punctual hairdresser and our timings don't align. I can't do your hair today and I won't be booking you back into my salon."

This experience has stayed with me for years. She was gutted and so was I, but if I hadn't said "no", it would've kept repeating itself. Even though I knew I was upsetting her, I chose to prioritise myself.

WHAT DID WE LEARN?
Lauren

In the particular situation of the drive home, I found that simply being honest worked. I still have work to do on not automatically saying "yes" to things that I know will make me resentful. There is a part of me that never feels that I am the most important person. I always feel my children's needs are more important than my own. I am deeply conditioned to not be "difficult", and I realised through this practice how uncomfortable and unused to saying "no" I am, but how relieved I feel when I am able to put a boundary in place.

Nicole

The woman in the salon more than likely walked away and bitched to all her friends about me, but that didn't make my boundary the wrong decision. Being true to myself means that not everyone will understand me and/or like me.

These practices build the relationship you have with yourself. They are not designed to make us more likeable; they are designed so that WE like who we are. No one else lives my life apart from me, so why live it by someone else's standards?

It is so important for me to stand up for myself rather than stress about whether everyone likes me. Whether people like me or not isn't something I have any control over, and nor should I. It's my business to like myself, and that's what I call self-care.

HOW TO STOP PEOPLE-PLEASING

Harriet Braiker writes in her book *The Disease To Please* (McGraw-Hill, 2002), "We have become addicted to the approval of others, and fearful of confrontation that we agree to every request – this comes with serious consequences."

A people-pleaser is a person who has an emotional need to please others, often at the expense of his or her own needs or desires and valuable time or feelings. On the surface, people-pleasers will be seen as likeable, kind and easy going, but more often than not, people-pleasers are struggling with their own boundaries and self-esteem. Being kind and thoughtful is a beautiful part of humanity, and we all want to think of ourselves as supportive to others; the problem lies when all the energy is moving in one direction, which is away from yourself, leaving you feeling very unbalanced.

People-pleasers tend to be good at tuning into what others are feeling. They are also generally empathetic, thoughtful and caring. These positive qualities are lovely, but only if used wisely, as they also come with a tendency to overachieve or a need to take control. People-pleasers want to be thought of as amenable and liked above all else. They often guess what other people want, or what will make someone else think favourably of them, and then act accordingly. Anytime we pretend to be or feel something that we aren't, we end up out of sync with ourselves. This is also the case when we are doing something to influence what others think of us, rather than being authentic. Always putting the needs of others before our own will become exhausting.

People-pleasers may think they're good at making other people happy, but their real talent lies in making *themselves* miserable. This need to please could be seen as a sign of weakness and, often unintentionally, gets taken advantage of. Instead of finding love and approval, you may experience the opposite: feeling devalued and resentful that everyone else's needs are more important than your own, and losing your sense of self. Eventually, you get into a state of imbalance in which everyone is benefiting from your kindness except you.

So, how do we strike that fine balance, and how do we know where we sit on the people-pleasing spectrum?

ARE YOU A PEOPLE-PLEASER?

There are a number of characteristics that people-pleasers tend to share. If you agree with three or more of the following statements, chances are you are a people-pleaser.

- You have a difficult time or feel guilty saying "no".
- You are preoccupied with what other people might think.
- You fear that turning people down will make them think you are mean or selfish.

- You agree to things you don't like or do things you don't want to do.
- You struggle with feelings of low self-esteem.
- You want people to like you, and feel that doing things for them will earn their approval.
- You're always telling people you're sorry.
- You take the blame, even when something isn't your fault.
- You rarely have free time for yourself and neglect your own needs because you are always doing things for other people.
- You pretend to agree with people even though you feel differently.
- You believe your own needs are not important.

SELF-CARE STEPS TO STOP PEOPLE-PLEASING

Step 1: Figure out when you are in people-pleasing mode

Sometimes it is so ingrained that we aren't aware we are even doing it, but without awareness, we can't change it.

Step 2: Think about why you are people-pleasing

Is it a habit? Is it because of a fear of not being liked or a fear of conflict? Is it a need for approval? The answer will allow you to move forwards and start putting all that energy into yourself.

Step 3: Accept you will not always be able to please everyone

This can be the hardest part of people-pleasing recovery, but it's crucial you are able to accept that putting your needs first won't always benefit the other person.

Step 4: Change the conversation from "What will *they* think?" to "What do *I* think?"

Change your internal conversation back to yourself and your needs.

Step 5: When someone asks for a favour, before saying "yes", ask yourself:

- *How much time will this take?*
- *Is this something I really want to do?*
- *Do I have time to do it?*
- *How stressed am I going to be if I say "yes"?*

Step 6: Prioritise

Consider where you want to spend your time, who you want to help, and what goals you are trying to accomplish. Knowing your priorities can help you determine whether or not you have the time and energy to devote to something else in your life.

Living with integrity can be a daunting thought. So, if you are worrying about being able to do this, we get it! Showing up as yourself and putting your own needs first can sometimes be socially unacceptable and scary, but we promise you it will be worth it. Being truthful about what you want and don't want in your life is a sign of bravery, and one you won't regret.

OUR EXPERIENCE

Lauren

I identify as a people-pleaser who is improving daily. I still have a handful of old relationships where I can fall into this pattern and I am still unpicking some approval-seeking issues within those. Since I turned 40, I have felt freer and more able to escape even these long-held patterns. So if you are younger and struggling with this, sit tight.

There was some "good girl" messaging that was prevalent when I was growing up, and I have a paper-thin line between being accommodating and people-pleasing. My practice began with a stark reminder of when the line is crossed over a particular weekend. I had 11 people coming for lunch on the Saturday and four people on the Sunday. One of the Sunday guests had a prior arrangement and, trying to be mindful and considerate of this person, I asked the other 14 people if they would mind switching days so that my guest could attend on the Saturday. Everyone agreed. So, after all of this swapping around, I open the front door on Saturday to my expected four guests but found only three standing there. The one person who had provoked this huge shuffling of arrangements had simply not shown up. They didn't text or call to let me know. They did, however, send their dog with a friend. As if to make a point, the dog immediately went and pooped on my living room rug. I had inconvenienced myself and many others because I was trying to be considerate. This person had not actually asked me to change the arrangements; I did that of my own accord. But in retrospect, I shouldn't have bothered as the respect I thought was between us was clearly not mutual. As I cleaned up the poo, the irony that the universe was giving me a clear lesson on not being shat on by others was not lost on me.

That same week, my husband got a text message from some friends of friends to say that they were having a big birthday party in a couple of weeks' time and they had room for more people, so we should come. I wasn't that keen as I didn't know anyone else who was going. I went through the steps laid out in this section and bought some time with a pause. I replied to say that I had two clients due to give birth over that week and couldn't commit right now as I had no idea what would be happening on the day. Once I put that holding space in place, I immediately felt more relaxed and happier. I weighed up whether I wanted to book a babysitter, find an outfit and work hard making small talk with strangers all night, instead of being home and rested. Thinking about what I needed that week in order to be on my game in case I was called out to a birth, I decided I could not risk it and, moreover, didn't feel compelled to attend a party where I was an afterthought. I very politely replied to the hosts and declined the invitation.

Nicole

I am not a people-pleaser. However, it has taken me years to get to this point; my hairdressing career helped me to tune into my schedule and not try to bend myself like a pretzel and please everyone else.

Nevertheless, one place where I found myself people-pleasing during the week was with a client when our political views didn't match, but I "nodded it in", as my friend Vanessa taught me. "Nodding it in" is when you shut your mouth, smile and nod so the other person thinks you're agreeing, but in reality, you are waiting for the moment to pass without confrontation. Not the best start.

Another example of when I people-pleased was when we had just started the podcast. Lauren and I were in the honeymoon phase of getting to know each other and the podcast production company we had partnered with to launch Self Care Club. The partnership itself was a strange dynamic, as it was more like we were employees rather than partners. We had a lot to learn, so we did as we were instructed without much questioning; and it was silently agreed that that's how things worked. It was getting to the point where I was feeling extremely constricted in the relationship, and felt Lauren and I needed to spread our wings and move towards our own vision for the show. A few situations arose where I wanted to say something, but I didn't, mainly because Lauren and I didn't know each other very well yet and, as she is conflict averse, I didn't want her to think I was a troublemaker.

Cut to a period of political unrest in the world, and I sympathetically commented on a friend's Instagram post about her struggle during this *period. Twenty minutes later the CEO of the production company called me and instructed me to remove the message as they didn't want any part of this political stance. I automatically apologised, told him I understood and removed my message (and sentiment) to my friend. This was people-pleasing on steroids!*

I ruminated about it for hours – the whole scenario sat so badly with me. Not only was this supposed "partner" monitoring our account (which was not part of the deal), he was also instructing me what to think and how to behave. But – here's the bit that gets to me – I gave him the power to do so. He was perfectly within his rights to inform me how he felt about it, and I was perfectly within my rights to do the same in response – but I didn't. I felt it easier to stand down and do as I was told. It has stayed with me for years as a moment where I regret not honouring myself. If that happened now, I think I would implement step three and four and say: "Thank you for your opinion, it's not one I agree with and removing my message doesn't work for me. Plus, please stop going through my account as it makes me very uncomfortable."

WHAT DID WE LEARN?
Lauren

As I get older, the disease to please is fading. Whether that is confidence, age, no longer feeling answerable to people, lived experience, being content and happy with who I am, feeling secure in my relationships or just no longer giving a fuck what other people think, it's just better and a far less exhausting and less stressful way to exist in the world. My intentions are always good, and I will always do my utmost to be considerate, kind and make other people happy – that brings me joy. It has taken me a long time to find my voice, and I am no longer willing to compromise myself, be a doormat or make myself unhappy or uncomfortable to accommodate everyone else.

Nicole

Being a boundaried person means that over the years I've been described as scary, frightening, or people have thought, "I wouldn't mess with her; she will tell you what she thinks" – it somehow always has a negative connotation, as if knowing what you want is a bad thing!

Not people-pleasing is a part of me that I am really proud of. There are a few people whose opinions really matter to me. I consider these people very carefully and I really do care what they think. This comes from a place of love and respect. Worrying about what anyone outside of that thinks of me is a dark road to nowhere.

TAKE-AWAY TIPS

Saying "no"
Focus on what you are saying "yes" to – it's a game changer.

Boundaries
Setting a boundary will cause discomfort – accepting that is a crucial part of the work. Your boundaries are yours, and no one has the power to dishonour them – only you. Use boundaries as an empowering force to create the life you want.

People-pleasing
You will never be able to control what people think, no matter how nice or amenable you are. It is a dead-end road that only leads to burnout. Your needs matter the most, as when you are thriving in your own life, it gives other people permission to do the same.

READER CHALLENGES

Lauren's challenge

Is there something in your diary you have committed to that you don't want to do? Consider cancelling it and put your own needs first.

Nicole's challenge

Say no to *everything* for 24 hours just to play with the idea of saying "no".

Will you pass the salt? No.

Can you babysit my dog? No.

Try it on for size and think of it as an experimental game: every time you say "no" you get a point. It will build resilience around using this necessary word.

Bonus challenge

People pleasing is hard.

Setting a boundary is hard.

Not having your needs met is hard.

Making a stand for yourself is hard.

When you slip into people-pleasing, ask yourself: *What can I do to honour my own wants and feelings here?*

Pick. Your. Hard.

Digital Detox

What's the first thing you do when you open your eyes in the morning? A whopping 88.6% of people check their phone within the first ten minutes of waking up.

Now, imagine your phone is not next to your bed or even in the room. If that makes you feel restless or uncomfortable, it may be time for a digital detox. This is defined as "a period of time during which a person refrains from using electronic devices such as smartphones or computers, regarded as an opportunity to reduce stress or focus on social interaction in the physical world".

This section isn't about bashing technology and social media. It's about being intentional in how and when you use it; learning to have boundaries around it is absolutely vital for protecting your mental health and your relationships.

As a society, we are all permanently plugged in. This has its benefits by allowing us to connect with people from all over the world, as well as keeping up with our family, friends and the Kardashians. Our phones have become so intrinsic to our lives that many of us feel uneasy if they are not around. There's even a term for the fear of being disconnected from your phone: nomophobia.

What we often ignore is the uncomfortable truth that technology use is a significant source of stress. The constant digital connection and need to keep checking emails, texts and social media amounts to a lot of pressure. There are also numerous studies around the use of technology being linked to sleep problems including poor sleep quality, inadequate amount of sleep and excessive daytime sleepiness.

What else has it done to us? Well, the average American adult attention span has dropped over the past decade from 12 seconds to a meagre 8 seconds – that's shorter than the attention span of a goldfish! Then there are the potential physical effects including hunched shoulders, neck pain, frown lines and raised blood pressure.

As for the emotional effects, well, for this we need to talk about something called "The iPhone effect". Studies have found that just having a phone present, even if you aren't actively checking it, lowers our empathy levels and reduces the quality of our interactions and conversation quality because our brains are just waiting for it to light up. As a result, we are not fully present with that person. Directing more energy to a phone than to the human being sitting opposite us is pretty pathetic.

Benefits of limiting device use to 30 minutes per day

- Improves wellbeing
- Decreases symptoms of loneliness
- Decreases symptoms of depression
- Lowers stress
- Improves sleep habits
- Improves your focus and brain function
- Boosts your physical activity
- Improves your posture
- Reduces eye strain
- Increases productivity
- Connects you to the real world
- Improves relationships

Sounds great, right? But, let's get real. It can be liberating for some people to switch off, while for others who rely on staying switched on for work, it might not be practical or possible.

A digital detox can take many forms. For the nomophobics among you, please know it doesn't have to be a complete break-up with your phone. It's about setting boundaries and using tech in a healthy way so you can be more present in your own life and for the people you love.

Tips for digital detoxing

- **Turn off push notifications**. Rather than being constantly pinged, set aside a specific time each day to check messages or "likes" and to catch up and send responses.
- **Designate tech-free hours**. Many of us feel "naked" when we're without our devices. Gradually reduce this discomfort by designating a certain time each day that's tech-free; for example, the first hour after you wake up.
- **Make your bedroom a no-tech zone**. Leave your phone outside the bedroom at night and invest in an old-fashioned alarm clock.
- **Read on actual paper**. Not only do books offer fewer distractions, but research suggests that when we read on paper, our minds process abstract information more effectively.
- **Limit yourself to one screen at a time**. When we're attempting to work or watch TV and we start scrolling through Instagram, our brains go a little haywire. Multitasking is really bad for you, as it takes several minutes to recalibrate our brains back to the original task. Make a habit of only looking at one screen at a time to improve concentration.
- **Switch your phone to silent when with others**. The distracting ping of your phone stops you from being in the present moment; remove the ping and you can focus all your attention on the person who has taken time out to be with you.

- **Set app limits**. Through your device settings, you can limit the time you spend on specified apps. You can find instructions for your operating system online.
- **Try "greyscaling"**. This converts your phone to black and white. One reason we love our phones is they are so vibrant. Our brains are automatically attracted to colour and shiny things. Smartphones allow you to change the settings so the entire phone looks grey, which makes it a whole load less fun to look at and thus encourages you to stop doom scrolling. Find your device's instructions online. We both did this and it totally works!

2

Self-love

Does the mere mention of self-love make you cringe and want to turn the page? Does it sound cheesy and a bit self-indulgent? Well, bear with us, just for one chapter, because learning to love yourself is one of the most powerful and important things you can do in life. As many psychology studies attest, self-love and self-compassion are vital for cultivating a healthy relationship with yourself and with others, and are imperative for your mental health and wellbeing.

Self-love is about being in charge of what love and happiness you bring into your life, regardless of who is or is not in your world. In the words of Ru Paul, "If you don't love yourself, how in the hell you gonna love somebody else?" In this chapter, we are focusing on the most important person in your life ... YOU.

Exploring ways to be more loving and compassionate towards ourselves are probably the most important practices of the whole book.

So, let's dive in.

WHAT IS SELF-LOVE?

Self-love means having respect and a high regard for your own thoughts, feelings, wants and happiness. It means taking care of your own needs first, and not sacrificing your wellbeing to please others or settling for less than what you deserve. It's not about being self-absorbed or narcissistic; it's about pushing through your self-limiting beliefs and living life on your terms. The most important relationship you will ever have in your life is the one with yourself.

BENEFITS OF SELF-LOVE

Think of self-love as cultivating a better relationship with yourself; once you have established that, the benefits are endless, and include:

- Better sleep
- Less likely to suffer with anxiety and depression
- Reduction in stress
- Less procrastination
- Trusting yourself and your decisions
- Feeling comfortable in your own skin
- Connected, close relationships
- A positive mindset, an essential ingredient for success in life

When you genuinely love yourself, you become willing to accept your life stages and take responsibility for your actions. Accepting your flaws and mistakes takes an enormous amount of courage. Self-love will allow you to accept every part of you. The good, the bad and even the saucy parts.

THE PRACTICES

There are many ways to practise self-love, and those we have selected are simple to do and have transformative results.

- **Being your own best friend**
- **Vabbing**
- **Self-celebration**

BEING YOUR OWN BEST FRIEND

We decided to dip our toe into the water slowly and start with a simple practice of self-love (so as not to scare Lauren off immediately). We realised that even on the most frantic of days we could both manage to spare a few seconds testing out being our own best friend.

When we questioned what practices to try, we kept coming back to kindness – how to be kind to ourselves, how important it was, but how poor we are at implementing it. We asked each other: *With whom in your life do you feel most loved and supported and who do you turn to when the chips are down?* The answer to both was our girlfriends. The women who know the bones of us. The women who in some cases knew us before we had boobs or could do joined-up handwriting. We know how to have a best friend and we know how to be a best friend to someone else; but what about giving all of that to yourself?

We are all taught from the beginning of our lives to be kind to others. But somewhere along the way, we forgot about the importance of being kind to ourselves. Let's face it, most of us do not offer the same kindness and compassion to ourselves as we do to other people. If we did, where would we even start?

Let's begin with a little exercise – don't worry, you don't need to change into a sports bra and leggings, or even get off the sofa.

Do you show yourself kindness?

1. Sit quietly and think about one of your closest friends or someone you love very dearly.

2. Tune into that person, imagine yourself with them, feel their energy, hear their voice, think about all the reasons you love them. Really let yourself sink into it.

3. Now imagine that person makes a mistake and messes up. Maybe they failed a test or said something they shouldn't have, and they are telling you about how bad they feel. What do you say to them?

   a) *"You fucking idiot!"*

   b) *"We are all human and everyone makes mistakes. Think of this as a learning curve. You can always try again and you'll be great."*

4. Now imagine this same person is having a bad day: they are struggling and feeling low or upset about something. What do you do?

   a) *Tell them they are pathetic and need to get a grip.*

   b) *Try to cheer them up, listen to them, give them a hug. Tell them it's okay to feel low, it's okay to mess up, it's okay to be having a bad day or a bad week. Make them feel supported and loved. (In a nutshell – show kindness and compassion.)*

We have assumed you chose answers "b". (If you didn't, well that requires a whole different book.)

Now, turn this exercise back on yourself.

What do you say to yourself when you make a mistake? Do you forgive yourself easily?

How do you treat yourself when you are feeling low or having a bad day? Probably not with the same kindness that you readily give to others. But there are so many ways that you can turn this around and be kinder and more compassionate to yourself.

Here are just a few ideas to get you started. Feel free to pick a few or even jot down some of your own.

- Speak kindly to yourself (this is a biggie).
- Daily affirmations.
- Make time for something that makes you smile.
- Eat your favourite food.
- Put on your favourite outfit.
- Spend time with people you love.
- Play your favourite song and sing loudly.
- Ask yourself what you need in that moment.
- Move your body in any way that feels good – dancing, walking, running, etc.

But why is it important to be kind to yourself? According to a growing body of research, being kinder to yourself can have a positive impact on overall health and wellbeing.

BENEFITS OF BEING YOUR OWN BEST FRIEND

Cultivating a more self-compassionate mindset:

- Improves your mental health
- Improves your physical health
- Improves your relationships
- Improves your concentration levels
- Makes you a happier person
- Makes you a better listener
- Makes you a better friend

SELF-CARE STEPS FOR BEING YOUR OWN BEST FRIEND

Step 1: Notice your unkind thoughts

When you are beating yourself up for doing something or not doing enough, ask yourself: *What would my best friend say to me right now?*

Or when you look in the mirror and tell yourself something mean about your face or your thighs (yes, we do it too), *instead* of doing that, ask yourself: *If this was my best friend looking in the mirror and being horrid to herself, what would I tell her?*

Step 2: Channel your "inner bestie"

Speak to yourself and treat yourself in the same way your best friend would speak, treat and love you.

OUR EXPERIENCE

Lauren

I have a harsh inner critic. This mean biatch likes things to be perfect and will bully me until they are. If I let things slide or standards slip, I beat myself up, and yet I would never expect this from others. I don't know why I imagine that anyone would judge me if I had a few dirty plates in the sink.

I got in at 1.30am on a weeknight. I had been out for dinner with my best friend and we had chatted away for hours, not noticing the time. I got up the next morning at 7am and looked in the mirror and my first and only thought was, I look shocking! Then I thought, No! That is so unkind. Imagine saying that with such a tone of disgust to your husband or your best friend in the morning. Okay, I look very tired, but I don't need to slag myself off. I put my makeup on and took my time getting ready. When I was done, I smiled at myself, and (feeling like a bit of an idiot) said a friendly "Good morning" out loud to my reflection – just like I would speak to my best friend.

The next day I was feeling frazzled. I had three meetings and loads of work still left to do. It was compounded by a whole afternoon and evening of chauffeuring my children around to various activities. At 6.30pm I was faced with the task of making a roast dinner and a dessert. On my last journey home, I diverted to the supermarket and bought a pack of ready-to-cook frozen roast potatoes, some ready-to-roast veg and a dessert. I then went home, bunged it all in the oven and sat down with a glass of wine while dinner cooked itself. For bonus points, I even bought myself a bunch of flowers. When dinner time came nobody even noticed that I hadn't peeled everything with my own fair hands. They loved the shop-bought cheesecake! I would never in a million years judge my BFF for doing this to help herself out after a long and busy day, or on any old day, or even if she did it every day! So why should I sit in judgement of myself?

Nicole

I was wiped out with Covid-19 and giving myself a hard time for feeling tired and lethargic. It was Sunday, the kids and my husband had gone out and I had one blissful hour in the house on my own. I told myself I had a dishwasher to unload, dinner to make and laundry to fold. Inner nasty voice alert.

So, I mentally called upon my inner best friend. She said, "Lady, you've been up since 6am. You've had a rubbish week, you're sick, let yourself sit down for an hour and watch Real Housewives." So, I cuddled the dog, watched six women fight and bitch about one another, and it was delightful. By the time everyone came home I felt much more rested and, to my surprise, the world didn't collapse.

The next day I had a text from my neighbour. The text went as follows: "Can you please ensure that your dog is not barking in the garden at unsociable hours. It has just woken up the entire family. It's highly disruptive to young children who need to be alert at school and for us at work. It has been going on for months."

I replied: "I assure you I have tried to since you last asked me. She is very rarely out at that time. It was a one-off. Let it go."

I was a tad abrupt. Normally, I would've been more polite, but this particular neighbour has a very brash manner, can be extremely un-neighbourly and gets my back up on my best of days. I ruminated about my reply all day, to the point of obsession. Later that day, another neighbour knocked at my door to tell me my dog doesn't stop barking and that a few of the neighbours had complained. Oh shit.

My snippy reply to my first neighbour still wasn't sitting right with me, and what I didn't need was a second one popping up moaning about the same issue. I fell deeply into a shame spiral.

I couldn't access my inner best friend – she left me hours ago, rolling her eyes and shaking her head somewhere between the neighbour's text and the second one turning up on the doorstep. I needed serious reinforcements, so called my actual best friend to pull me out of the rabbit hole. She said, "Nicole. You've not left the house for days, you're overdramatising. Just text the neighbour and apologise for the tone of your text, stop the dog barking and the whole thing will go away."

I did what she said. She was right. Safe to say I failed this practice.

WHAT DID WE LEARN?
Lauren

This practice was about being a bit more accepting of myself as the imperfect human being that I am. I had to take responsibility for being my own worst critic and for setting rules and regimes that are not easy to attain all of the time. I learnt that as I am the one who created the rules, I am also the one with the power to dismantle them. I am the only person judging me by standards that I have set for myself. Nobody dies if you serve pre-prepared side dishes and dessert.

Nicole

Having that constant question of: What would my best friend say to me right now? is a lovely prompt of something far kinder than my inner bully. It changed everything in an instant (or would have, had I practiced it properly). Automatically, it gets you in touch with something supportive. I am still working on this but in time I know it will help create a more compassionate relationship with myself.

VABBING

Take a deep breath and keep an open mind as we delve into what is possibly the most controversial practice that we have ever tested on the show.

If you are the proud owner of a vagina, you will know that it produces a lot of useful secretions. These secretions keep it happy, healthy and – most importantly – lubricated. The secretions are helpful for comfortable intercourse, and can also be used as an indicator of where you are in your menstrual cycle. But what if we told you there was another use for your vaginal fluids? That they could make you feel sexy, or even attract a potential partner? Welcome to the world of "vabbing".

What the hell is "vabbing"?, we hear you ask, nervously. Vabbing is a word that combines "vagina" and "dabbing", and it refers to dabbing your vaginal fluid on your body as if it was perfume. The intention is to make you more attractive to others. As with perfume, you are supposed to "dab" the pressure points behind your ears and on your wrists. The idea is that vabbing attracts potential partners, because vaginal secretions contain pheromones that play a role in mating behaviour.

BENEFITS OF VABBING

Partaking in vabbing can:

- Feel empowering and sexy – this might be down to pheromones, but it could also be a placebo effect
- Increase confidence levels – when you project confidence, it makes you more attractive to others
- Be fun – and a bit naughty

Fun and Unfun Facts

Is it safe? Yes. Perfectly safe unless you have an active STD. However, if you have bacterial vaginosis (BV), your vaginal discharge might smell quite unpleasant, making it a vastly less-than-ideal perfume. In that case, please skip the vabbing my darling and make an appointment with your doctor.

This was the one practice that could have ended our relationship. Lauren had been wanting to test it out since the podcast began, while Nicole made it clear it was a hard no. But after a year of acclimatising Nicole with practices like vaginal steaming, she finally agreed. We recorded this episode at home rather than in the studio for privacy; the irony being that this was a complete illusion of privacy as the podcast was then available on every platform forever for absolutely anybody and everybody to listen to.

Are you still with us, or have you turned to the next chapter in horror or chucked the book across the room in disgust?

If you are brave, ready and willing to give it a go, here's how you do it.

SELF-CARE STEPS TO VABBING

Step 1: Hygiene
Firstly, wash your hands as you don't want to transfer any germs to your vagina. If you are like Nicole and never read a manual or followed an instruction, we've included this step as it's best to leave no room for confusion here.

Step 2: Application
Insert a finger or two in your vagina, and dab the fluid on your pressure points; this could be on your neck, behind your ears, or on your wrists.

Step 3: Hygiene again
Wash your hands again, and you're good to go!

OUR EXPERIENCE

Lauren
I was totally nonplussed at the concept of vabbing and curious to try it out, so when the perfect occasion presented itself, I decided to do a stealth vabbing session weeks before we were recording the episode. Nicole and I were having our Christmas get-together (dinner with a couple of guys we work with). I vabbed before I left home. I arrived first and the manager came over with a drinks menu and then just wouldn't leave me alone! About 20 minutes later, everyone at the table noticed something

was going on. This debonair Italian guy was just sniffing around me – not literally! But I really had his attention.

Nicole was totally bemused, she kept asking me what the hell was going on and if something had happened before I arrived. I couldn't say anything because I didn't want our male colleagues to know that I was sporting my own vagina scent at the office Christmas party. But my endless blushing was giving it away. Nicole had her suspicions, but told me later that she was happier living in denial of what I had done. All in all, I would say that the first vabbing experiment got a big tick.

The second time I tried it I was milling around at home on a Sunday. I was resplendent in a baggy tracksuit and glasses, looking undoubtedly irresistible, yet my husband left his usual spot on the sofa to sidle up to me. I weighed up whether or not to tell him the reason he felt drawn to me like a moth to a flame, but decided to keep him in the dark, just in case he decided I had gone a step too far this time.

The third and final time I vabbed was before a day out in town, just to see what would happen. The answer: absolutely nothing. My tube journey was uneventful. I didn't get any extra attention in the shops or at lunch. Although, late in the day, I found myself in a newsagents, and there was a group of young guys in there. One of them turned around and said earnestly, "What a beautiful woman you are." I strongly suspect he had spent all afternoon drinking in Soho, as I can assure you that random men do not make a habit of telling me I'm beautiful. For some reason it made me quite cross as I was nearly old enough to be his mother, and frankly it took all my willpower not to say to him, "Don't flirt with me in a newsagent. If I told you I had my own vaginal secretions smeared behind my ears what would you say to that, eh? Go tell that to your mates!"

After that, I decided I had had quite enough attention for the year, and left vabbing alone.

Nicole

I was horrified at the thought of us being known as "those vabbing women". I went into the practice thinking this was probably more suitable for a single person. I didn't need to go out and attract a horny 20-year-old in a nightclub on a Saturday night.

Let me clarify: I don't think vaginas are dirty or wrong in any way. They give life and are pretty magical, but I just don't think you need to smear your secretions all over your face and neck. For me, how you feel in yourself and what you are exuding is the key, and I couldn't see how rubbing myself all over myself would build confidence.

Unsurprisingly, my practice got off to a slow pace. I was so caught up in what people would think that I just couldn't do it. I couldn't, I wouldn't. I went round in circles and this carried on for a few days with a few "I hate Lauren"s thrown in for good measure. I knew Lauren would be pheromoned up to the eyeballs and glowing in the radiance of her own vagina, but for me this was an edge. However, I was running out of time.

I was out for a quick bite to eat with my husband, had my favourite jumpsuit on and was actually feeling great. I decided it was now or never. So, I went to the loo and you can guess the rest. I came back to the table, we sat, we had dinner and nothing happened. He didn't lean over the table to kiss me, and there were no 19-year-olds humping my leg. And no, I didn't tell him. After dinner, I had to go and pick up my kids who happened to be at the synagogue at a cinema night. I stood there waiting for them to come out thinking, "I am vabbing outside a place of worship." I had never felt more aware of my vagina in my life. I was mortified. I texted Lauren to tell her I hated her. She replied: "Mazaltov!"

The next day I was going to a gym called Barry's Bootcamp. I vabbed and rationalised it by telling myself that as it wasn't my usual gym, it was the first time I had been there and I didn't know a soul. As I arrived, a gorgeous six-foot Adonis of a man came up and said, "Nicole, come with me." I thought, "Oh hello! This vabbing business might be alright after all." He started taking me through how the treadmills worked and where the weights were, and all I could think was, "Can you smell my vagina?" He was very, very attentive throughout the session, but it was probably because I was new to the place rather than the fact I was wearing my own scent as perfume.

WHAT DID WE LEARN?
Lauren
I think this is a fascinating experiment. Why not be paving the way for women who may feel terrified to try this, but want to attract a partner, or just empower themselves? As a doula I have spent 16 years in the vagina business. To me, they are an incredible, magical, life-giving bit of anatomy. There is such a stigma that a vagina has an unpleasant scent (or even any scent at all), and that needs dispelling.

I learnt that sometimes there is a little part of me that quite enjoys doing something a bit subversive. It tapped into the side of me that on occasion likes to be a bit naughty.

Nicole
It feels like a very brazen and bold thing to do, but once I got past it, I liked the idea of doing something a bit rebellious, that was quite empowering.

It did give an extra boost to my self-esteem, like a fabulous outfit or great make up does. If you are single and dating, then it's an interesting experiment. Plus, it makes a great dinner conversation topic.

Nicole: *Lauren, are we done with the vagina stuff now? (Please.)*

SELF-CELEBRATION

Tell us the truth: when was the last time you celebrated yourself? Was it when you were offered that new job? On a milestone birthday? Or when you got married? Or have you never truly celebrated yourself?

Special moments are worthy of celebration, but you don't need a milestone to celebrate yourself. You are worth celebrating every day. In fact, celebrating the small wins and small moments in life is just as important as celebrating the big ones. Small wins lead to larger ones, and they need to be recognised in order to encourage you forward.

If you're reading this and feeling uncomfortable, we are not surprised. Do you feel as if you can't or don't know how to celebrate yourself? Join the club.

Most girls are taught from a very young age to be modest and polite, and are told that discussing small personal wins will come across as conceited and big-headed. This invariably causes those little girls to grow up into women who are unable to acknowledge their strengths and achievements for fear of being disliked or unappealing.

Belittling or hiding what you have achieved and keeping your successes to yourself does not serve you, nor does it serve anyone else. It just continues the cycle and narrative that women need to stay small and unassuming to be likeable.

Self-celebration is an important life skill that none of us are taught. So, in the spirit of self-love, get your celebration knickers on and let's go.

So, what do we mean when we talk about self-celebration? It's about recognising and celebrating who you are right now – not your future self or the person you wish you were. It is your own personal celebration of who you are and where you are and what it took to get yourself here. Think of it as a secret weapon in your back pocket to encourage and empower you. You do not need balloons or a cake (although these are totally encouraged). You can celebrate yourself anytime, anywhere and for any reason.

Are you still feeling ill at ease with this concept?

> **Lauren:** Yes, a bit.
> **Nicole:** I was talking to the reader.

Let's first dispel what self-celebration is NOT. It's not arrogant, narcissistic or attention seeking. It's not about proving your worth to others. It is not to show that you are better than anybody else. It's not about anybody but YOU.

This practice requires you to be truthful with yourself; this can be a tough mode to step into at times as a lot reveals itself when you do. It's often stuff you may not want to look at or have been avoiding. But please know, if this happens – in the spirit of the practice – you get to celebrate that you began to lean into the resistance, because that process can be rough. There is always something to celebrate; we just ask that you stay honest with yourself and know this practice helps you grow and elevate. Self-celebration will never keep you stuck.

BENEFITS OF SELF-CELEBRATION

Practicing regular self-celebration:

- Supports you to know yourself in a deeper, more positive way
- Helps you understand the wonder you bring to the world, which helps build more self-love
- Increases confidence – the more that you celebrate yourself, the bigger the confidence boost
- Allows you to be proud of who you are
- Reminds us to enjoy the journey.

I know, we said "journey" – apologies. But, clichés aside, when we spend all our time focused on the outcome and in the "doing" part, we forget to see what's actually happening. To get all the clichéd phrases out of the way in one paragraph, we are human beings, not human doings. So, take a moment every day, stop what you are doing, celebrate, and savour the moment.

Self-celebration also reminds us to be grateful for what we are and what we have. Gratitude was the very first practice we tested for the podcast and turned out to be one of the most important – it is vital to our happiness and fulfilment. When we celebrate ourselves, we are taking that moment to be genuinely grateful for our life just as it is.

SELF-CARE STEPS TO SELF-CELEBRATION

Step 1: Write a list of your accomplishments

Try to find the best moment in your day and celebrate it. Look at your daily accomplishments: see what you have achieved rather than what you have not.

Step 2: Write yourself a letter

Take step one a little further and write yourself a letter. This may make you cringe a little inside, but sometimes the best way to celebrate yourself is to write down what makes you unique. You can be proud of yourself, and you do not have to show it to anybody. Feel free to pop the letter in your journal or on your vision board for inspiration as and when you need it.

Step 3: Question yourself

"What am I celebrating today?" is an informative question that can get you out of negative self-talk and into something more rewarding. So often our default mode is to find the ways in which we are not enough or not doing enough, but this simple question allows you to see where you are winning at life.

Step 4: Buy yourself something special

Start a small savings pot for your dream purchase or you could just celebrate with something frivolous that makes you happy, like a bunch of flowers.

Step 5: Share your successes

Sharing your successes with your friends and family – telling them about something that you're proud of – is not showing off. People who love you want to know about and celebrate your achievements with you, just like you want to hear about and celebrate theirs. For bonus points, accept any compliments that might follow. The trickiest part to compliments is receiving them.

OUR EXPERIENCE

Lauren

This practice came at a serendipitous time. Not only had we just agreed and signed the book deal, but it was my birthday the next day. Aside from dinner that evening, I had no intention of celebrating. Nicole however, had other ideas. As we always spend Wednesdays together, she had the hump that a) I wasn't seeing her and b) I wasn't celebrating, so she took charge. I felt guilty and also super-indulgent spending a whole weekday celebrating myself – after all, I'm not five. Nicole coaxed me into a trip into town, and we ended up in one of those shops where you want absolutely everything you touch, until you look at the price tag. I picked up a coat and the store manager told me that it was the only one left and that it was 40% off. Even with the discount, it was far more than I would ever spend on a whim. I tried it on and it was the perfect fit, made me feel totally put together and was everything I had ever wanted in a winter coat. The manager then said that, as it was my birthday, she would extend the discount to 50%. I asked her to put it aside and went to think about it over lunch.

At lunch, for a treat Nicole ordered us both a glass of bubbly – the ultimate celebration drink! As we sat, I reasoned that at the grand old age of 45 I should have an investment piece in my wardrobe. We had made a pact that when we signed the book deal, we would each buy ourselves a celebratory gift. It seemed that the coat was destined to be mine. I bought it feeling happy and deserving.

It was time to try Step 5: Share your successes. Despite having the deal agreed for this book, for some reason I could not talk about it or tell anyone. I rationalised this by telling myself that it was hard to put across in words what it feels like to achieve your lifetime ambition: to write a book! I was still processing it, while also feeling guilty and weird about keeping the news to myself. I then realised how selfish I was being by not sharing my achievement and my joy with the people who loved me the most; and I thought about how hurt they would be if they found out via social media or from somebody else. So, I began a series of messages and awkward phone calls – all of which were met with joy, praise and pride. I did accept the compliments as best I could. But the best thing I discovered was that as heart-warming as it was to get the feedback, everyone's reaction was actually irrelevant because this was something that I had achieved for myself, and my celebration was my own.

Nicole

My practice week started with the book deal too – what a perfect way to practise self-celebration. But, let's backtrack. A few months before, we sent our book proposal off to potential publishers, and even pencilled in a celebratory dinner for the date that our agent had suggested we would get a deal. The day before the planned dinner date, there wasn't a sniff of any interest from any publishers, so we begrudgingly cancelled the table. Obviously, seeing how you are currently reading the very book I am talking about, an offer did eventually come in – two in fact. We were delighted – it was a huge dream of ours. We had a hug and that was it. We sat back at our laptops and carried on with our work. It didn't occur to either one of us to rebook our planned night out and go celebrate. We let a wonderful opportunity pass us by. No champagne toast, no slap-up meal, no celebration.

Pathetic. It was, without a doubt, one of the biggest moments of my professional life and I let it pass me by. #fail

To make up for the above, I opted to try Step 2: Write yourself a letter. I debated long and hard whether to share the letter here. Making my personal celebrations public is totally out of my comfort zone and goes against everything we as women are taught. It felt brazen and cocky, but I figured that's what made it so necessary.

Did I want my daughters to understand their power, their achievements, their efforts, their successes? The answer to that was glaringly obvious. So, I decided to share mine with you, and break the cycle for myself, my daughters and hopefully for you. With my hands over my eyes, here is my letter to myself.

The 12-year-old girl inside of me, who was told she was stupid and lazy, who failed at school, has come a long way. She would be amazed and proud at what the woman inside her has achieved: hairdresser, coach, podcaster and now author.

My Values

Truth. This is a vital part of my life, and I try my best to be an honest mother, wife, sister, daughter and friend.

Integrity. It is my greatest and most trusted friend, and I allow it to guide me through life – knowing what feels right and what doesn't.

Purpose. Whatever I am doing and surrounding myself with has to hold value and passion. Friendships, relationships, habits, boundaries, thought processes and behaviours are all part of that.

Growth. It has not been a smooth path (I don't think it's meant to be), but it has been a liberating one. There are people I have loved and lost along the way, and this has at times left me heartbroken. I learnt that prioritising myself cost me those relationships, but it helped me become the full version of me, so I can finally say I am thankful to those people. I look at who I have around me today and it makes me very proud. The people I have consciously chosen in my life love and support me as I do them, and those relationships add richness to my world.

Wellbeing. The daily choices I make for myself honour my health, wellbeing, self-respect and self-love.

Authenticity. I have learnt to take up space. and not only is it okay, it is necessary. The words I speak, the thoughts I think, the actions

I take, the feelings I feel – they all matter. I matter! It has taken years to find that comfort and permission to be me, but I now gift it to myself unapologetically.

Today, I choose to celebrate it all. I celebrate all of me. The good, the bad, the failings, the losses, the wins, the beauty, the flaws and the ongoing learning. If I met myself at a dinner party, I would want to be my friend.

And breathe.

WHAT DID WE LEARN?
Lauren
Self-celebration doesn't magically happen. I had to intentionally take a pause to look at my own achievements. I haven't lived an extraordinary life, and my celebrations may seem small or they may seem impressive depending on the person viewing them. But that is irrelevant, as what is important is that all these achievements belong to me. Once I got over the uncomfortable novelty and discomfort of being my own hype woman, I surprised myself by feeling genuinely proud of them.

Nicole
Don't let opportunities to celebrate moments pass you by. They are an amazing landmark of your life. Hiding from our strengths only adds to the narrative that women need to remain unassuming and small to be likeable.

Celebration is a beautiful and important path to self-discovery and self-love (and probably a bit more useful than vabbing).

TAKE-AWAY TIPS

Being your own best friend

Having that anchoring thought of *What would I tell my best friend if she was experiencing this?* gives not only a different perspective, but a much kinder one. This is vital for developing a stronger relationship with yourself.

Vabbing

It's exciting and naughty and really shocks people. Wearing your own scent can have a strangely empowering effect on your mood.

Self-celebration

This is a fundamental practice of growth and self-love. As uncomfortable as it can be, make sure you allow some space for it in your self-care toolkit. Ask yourself every day, *What am I celebrating today?*

READER CHALLENGES

Lauren's challenge

Try vabbing, it's a bit risqué but a lot of fun. Try it for a first date, a date with your long-term partner (whether you choose to tell them or not is up to you) or just when you want to exude some inner confidence. If you need any more persuading; following the release of the vabbing podcast episode, one woman wrote in to tell us that she vabbed and successfully seduced a woman she had been attracted to for months who is now her girlfriend! Another woman told us that she vabbed before a date night with her husband which was so successful that they are pretty sure this was the night they conceived their first child!

Nicole's challenge

Write the celebration letter and read it aloud to someone you love and trust. It may be uncomfortable, but it will change the way you see yourself.

Comparison

Comparison is one of the most prevalent reasons why social media is linked with negative body image, sleep issues, anxiety and depression. Social comparison is a form of sociological self-esteem, where we derive our sense of self through comparing ourselves with others. Psychologist Leon Festinger's social comparison theory states that humans can't define themselves independently, but only in relation to other individuals. And we compare ourselves to other people on social media all the time: we rate our appearance, possessions, relationships, home, holidays, social lives, performance, bank balance, and even our problems and vulnerabilities.

Festinger argues people have a tendency to make downward social comparisons with those who are worse off or less skilled than them, and this can raise their self-esteem. Conversely, upward social comparisons can reduce self-esteem. Simply log in to Instagram and you will be served up a universe full of endless opportunities to compare yourself against others. Your uneventful, average day is always going to seem shoddy compared with the "greatest hits" of people on your feed who all seem to be having, "like, the most 'mazing time" and they are "totes hashtag blessed". This is when you run the risk of falling headfirst into the comparison trap, which leads to you imagining others' experiences as being far superior to your own.

This comparison trap is mainly packed to the brim with negative consequences. As Theodore Roosevelt said, "Comparison is the thief of joy"; it makes us feel disappointed with our lot in life and can lead to low self-esteem, low self-confidence and general dissatisfaction. You lose the ability to celebrate your achievements as that 10k walk you did suddenly doesn't seem so cool compared to "Sophie" who spent Sunday climbing Snowdon for charity (while looking like a hottie in her Lululemon leggings).

With comparison, you are at risk of losing your sense of self and what makes you unique. You may also lose some self-compassion and self-confidence, which could affect your mental wellbeing.

Let's not also forget that comparison also often ends in resenting others and can quickly turn to judgement. *How does Sophie even afford those leggings and who does she think she is anyway?* Comparisons are hardly ever fair. It is like comparing a snail and a cheetah in a race – both will run the race, but will do so in their own unique way.

Why do we compare ourselves with people who we don't know? We don't have all the facts, just what they choose to show us. You won't see the struggles that they may be facing; they may be like the proverbial swan – calm on the surface but paddling like crazy underneath the water.

Comparison is a waste of time and energy. You can't compare yourself to any other human on this planet because you are unique. Focus on yourself and your own journey, because you can only control one life and that's your own.

So how do we escape this habit and learn to live life on our own terms? If you are feeling down because of social media, remind yourself that it's other people's highlight reel. They are not putting up photos of the spot on their chin, or their bad hair day. Practise gratitude, celebrate aspects of yourself that have nothing to do with appearance and embrace your perfect imperfections that make you the beautifully unique person that you are.

Tips to stop comparison

- **Turn comparison into inspiration**. We tend to focus on other people's success, not on the thousands of hours they've spent preparing and working for their achievement. Let other people's triumphs be an inspiration for what you can be and do. Treat someone else's holiday to the Bahamas as a reminder of what you want for yourself – use it to motivate you to save up for that holiday.
- **Compare yourself with yourself**. If you want to compare yourself with someone, make it you. Are you doing better than you were last year, last month? Are you trying your best? What can you do to improve your quality of life? How can you be kinder to yourself than you were yesterday? You are the only person living your life, so make sure it follows your rules.
- **Celebrate abundance in others**. When you see others who have what you want, celebrate it! Recognise that when you see others' abundance it's a sign that yours is getting closer to coming to you. This is a classic manifesting tool. Be conscious about your energy and thoughts. Remember abundance breeds abundance. If you stay in comparison it will bring more of the same.
- **Spring clean your social media accounts**. Many people forget that your social media feed is something you curate for yourself. If you follow an account that is no longer making you feel positive or makes you feel insecure or annoys you, then take one second to unfollow and delete

them from your online life. If you can't unfollow for political friendship reasons then just mute the account.

- **Practice "Driftwood Theory"**. Author Gabby Bernstein recommends this: Choose to see the people who have what you want as a reflection of what's to come. Let their success mirror back to you what you're ready to receive. Pay attention to the positive clues in your life showing you that your desires are on the way to manifesting. The common human response to seeing someone else have what we want can be jealousy, or if they have it you may translate that as "because they have it, that means I can't".

- **Run your own race**. Do things for your own goals on your own terms. Your life is lived by you, and you only.

3

Confidence

Confidence is an innate belief in oneself. It comes from your thoughts, your behaviour and the words you speak. It means feeling sure of yourself and your abilities. Having confidence helps you to achieve your goals, cope with challenges, make you more likely to take risks and embrace new opportunities with a sense of certainty and self-assurance.

Confidence also improves your decision-making. It helps you make choices that are in line with your own values rather than making decisions based on fear or other people's desires.

Confidence creates self-love, which can support you to walk away from toxic relationships or habits that don't serve you. It enables you to curate a life that works for you on your own terms.

Confidence, or lack of, dictates how you hold yourself, how you see yourself, how you relate to others and how you show up in the world. It is a vital cornerstone into your whole being. So, think of this chapter as a lesson in how to harness your inner badass.

BENEFITS OF CONFIDENCE

The benefits of confidence to your wellbeing are endless, and include:

- Less stress and anxiety
- Better mental health
- More resilience
- Strong social skills
- Strong communication skills
- Strong boundaries
- Healthier relationships
- Better physical wellbeing
- More energy
- Better performance at work
- An openness to try new things
- An increased happiness and sense of wellbeing

HOW CONFIDENT ARE YOU?

If you are not sure where you sit on the confidence spectrum, we have broken it down for you with signs of high confidence (think Beyoncé) versus low confidence (think Eeyore). Tick the ones that you feel apply to you.

Signs of confidence

The more you tick, the more you'll be singing "Run the World (Girls)".

You are comfortable in your own skin	
You are comfortable with who you are	
You trust yourself	
You are decisive	
You have good boundaries	
You are comfortable with saying "no"	
You are open to feedback	

You are resilient	
You believe in your abilities and in yourself	
Others believe in you	
You don't compare yourself to others	

Signs of low confidence

The more you tick, the more you'll be hanging out in the 100-Acre Wood.

You feel unsure of your abilities	
You question your decisions and judgments	
You avoid trying new things	
You struggle with decision-making	
You use negative self-talk	
You avoid social situations	
You joke about yourself in a negative way	
You focus on your negatives and ignore your achievements	
You blame yourself when things go wrong	
You compare yourself to others	

So, where do you sit? If you ticked numerous points on the low-confidence list, the practices in this chapter will really support you in building more self-confidence.

It's important to remember that low confidence is not an ingrained flaw, and it doesn't have to define you. The good news is: confidence can be learnt and practised. It begins with becoming more self-aware, changing your mindset, and learning to bring your full, beautiful, flawed, human self to every situation.

This chapter will guide you in tangible ways to achieving confidence in your everyday life. Building and maintaining confidence requires practice and self-reflection. With some time, tools and self-trust, we believe you can develop the confidence needed to live a better life.

Our age has definitely helped improve our confidence – thank you, over-40s club! But we both felt there was still room for improvement. Nicole will openly admit she can struggle with anxiety and overwhelm, and Lauren has a nasty voice inside of her that frequently needs shutting down.

THE PRACTICES

To improve our confidence and yours, we have selected practices designed to help you walk through your life with more self-assurance and to support you to create a powerful relationship with yourself; because, after all, how you relate to yourself is how you relate to everything and everyone.

- **Making micro-connections**
- **How to stop apologising**
- **Asking for what you want**

MAKING MICRO-CONNECTIONS

Micro-connections are small moments of connection that happen between two or more people. It can be a simple exchange with a stranger in a supermarket, a moment of shared laughter, a doorstep chat with the postman about the weather. Essentially, it is a mini moment of joy, kindness or connection passed between one another. Micro-connections are not big relationship moments, but rather the small interactions that happen every day. They teach us to appreciate the moments in life that we are often too busy to notice, and leave us with a feeling of warmth and kinship with humanity.

Leading busy lives, these special moments often get overlooked or dismissed as an everyday occurrence; but when you look again, when you take the moment to appreciate them or, better still, create them, the power they hold can be quite magical. Our brain recognises this and rewards us.

THE SCIENCE STUFF

Oxytocin is a neuro-hormone known as the "love chemical", which is essential for social bonding. This critical neuropeptide helps us to bond with others, and is released every time we make a micro-connection. It builds trust, reduces physical stress and raises self-confidence. Having a higher oxytocin level, will boost your endocrine and immune systems, which in turn can improve your overall physical health.

Professor Barbara Frederickson and Professor John Gottman's research demonstrates that three social connections a day not only helps fill our emotional buckets but also helps build resilience. They found that a three-to-one positivity ratio makes us feel like we belong. It also provided a positive impact on resilience and mental health.

Social media can emphasise our own insecurities so if you feel like others are living their best lives, engaging with a ton of besties and attending exclusive parties while you are feeling lonely or left out, then micro-connections are a brilliant way to support you to engage with the physical world around you. They are especially effective if you are socially anxious or suffering with low mood and anxiety, as a micro-connection is a small, quick task that has a lasting benefit on your wellbeing. With oxytocin surging in your brain, the sensation may encourage you to reach out again. Consider micro-connections as small building blocks, moving you in the direction of deeper and more meaningful interactions.

BENEFITS OF MAKING MICRO-CONNECTIONS

Micro-connections can create:

- Feelings of gratitude
- Reduced anxiety and depression
- Better regulated emotions
- Higher self-esteem and empathy

- Improved immune systems
- Feeling more connected to the world around you
- Feeling less isolated
- More kindness in the world

SELF-CARE STEPS FOR MAKING MICRO-CONNECTIONS

Step 1: Seek out opportunities

Each day look for three opportunities to connect with others. It could be a relative, friend, colleague or complete stranger. Each interaction can be with the same person or with three different people. Approach this with warmth and positivity.

Step 2: Make eye contact and smile

This can be with a stranger or someone you are very familiar with, but it's an important step in a world where we spend the majority of time with our face stuck in our phones. You'll be amazed at the ripple effect.

Step 3: Ask a question

A simple "How's your day going?" to the Amazon delivery driver or the barista making your coffee goes a long way. People appreciate being noticed.

Step 4: Notice the energy

Keep track of how these connections (and the oxytocin hit) make you feel. This is the juicy part we love. When you walk away from your micro-connection, there should be a subtle warmth running through you. It may lift your mood. Take a moment to breathe it in. Each night think about the interactions and how much you felt connected to the other person.

OUR EXPERIENCE

Lauren

There is no denying that I am a natural chatterbox. It comes in handy when you host a podcast for a living! I will chat to anyone, anywhere – often much to the horror and embarrassment of my children. I talk to people behind me at the post office counter, at checkout queues, in shops, in parks and in cafés. I get a lot of joy from the small interactions of everyday life; a friendly chat can ease the boredom of any queue, and there is no long-term obligation to the relationship. This practice was like water off a duck's back to me.

I walk my dog every morning in my local woods. Dog walking is probably the most common and easiest place to find micro-connections, and even if you don't own a dog, anyone walking will usually be more than happy to stop and let you pet theirs and have a chat. I often see the same people out with their dogs, which leads to at least two or three daily interactions before 10am. The first morning of the practice week was no exception. In addition to the regulars, I wished a cheery good morning to a couple out Nordic walking and to an elderly man seated alone on a bench who gave Barker a pat and a biscuit.

The next day, I was at a local market, and stopped at a café in the middle of the square for a drink. I noticed an older woman sitting at the next table resplendent in a velour tracksuit, perfectly coiffed white hair and a pair of mint green Cartier sunglasses. I leaned over and told her that they looked utterly fabulous. "Darling", she told me, "they were a tenner from a stall close by. I've got a pair in every colour!" We agreed that this was a secret she should keep to herself as she could totally pass them off as legit.

The following day, I was having lunch with a friend, and there was a girl sat at a table nearby wearing a pair of electric green cowboy boots. I couldn't resist going over to her to talk about them; I told her she was the coolest girl in the street. She laughed and I went back to my sandwich, wearing my not-very-exciting trainers; both of us feeling uplifted at our fun exchange.

I was well into and thoroughly enjoying this practice now, with each day bringing a different micro-connection. On day four, my neighbour and I both returned home to our street at the same time. I asked how he was and he broke out in a huge grin and told me that his wife was expecting another baby. He enjoyed sharing his happy news, and we had a quick chat about the pregnancy.

Finally, I was on the tube, and a couple of older women were seated next to me. One of them had a tickling cough that just wouldn't ease, so I took a cough sweet out of my handbag and offered it to her. She smiled and accepted it with thanks.

Nicole

I like to think of myself as a friendly person. I am always happy to chat to strangers in the woods (that sounded creepier than I wanted) when I'm walking my dog, or in a shop, to the barista or my postman, to give a few examples. So this didn't feel like a stretch.

It was 6:30pm on a Tuesday night and, yet again, my youngest daughter had broken her glasses, so off I went to the optician. I was pissed off; this was the third time in a month her glasses had broken and they were costing a small fortune to fix. At the opticians, a lovely woman approached me. I grumpily explained the situation, prepared to be hit with a hefty bill. She looked for us on their system, we weren't on it, and I was becoming more irritated by the minute. She went to speak with her supervisor, I kept my head in my phone. She came back smiling and looked on the system once again.

She was lovely, I was not. She made conversation, I tried not to. She practised micro-connections and I refused to play. While she trawled through the system, I mentioned coming in last week with my very moody 12-year-old and (mortifyingly) she remembered us. Sometimes my daughter throwing an unreasonably hormonal strop has its advantages. She got up from the table, went over to the counter, picked up a new pair of frames and handed them to me. I was awestruck.

She said, "I am so sorry we couldn't find you on the system, here's a brand-new pair." I felt ashamed of my behaviour. I snapped myself out of my own 12-year-old strop and said, "Thank you so much for your help. I wasn't expecting this and I'm very grateful."

She smiled and my mood instantly lifted – not because I got what I wanted, but because she was kind and generous in spirit and she reminded me what a micro-connection should look like.

The following day, I was walking in the park when a dog walker walked past with her very playful puppy. I just had to stop and stroke the little bundle of joy. We had a brief chat, mostly involving my dog growling at the sweet puppy and me telling the stranger how beautiful her pooch was. Now, I would've done this anyway, micro-connection week or not, but this time I was doing it with awareness. I tapped into how I felt after the short interaction and it felt great. I felt warm, connected and better off for taking that moment to share a positive, sweet interchange with a stranger.

WHAT DID WE LEARN?

Lauren

I never go a day without at least five to ten micro-connections. They are a genuine part of my self-care and never fail to make me happy. Often, if I am having a bad morning and walking the dog in a bit of a funk, just one connection can change my mood and my mindset. They are such a quick fix for raising your spirits or getting you out of a negative headspace. I have a heightened awareness that there is a loneliness epidemic going on, especially for elderly people. You don't know if that micro-connection might be the only conversation they will have that day, so I make it a daily mission when I am out and about to say hello, chat about the weather or compliment them on a lovely-coloured coat or scarf.

Nicole

The noticing makes all the difference. Bringing awareness to these micro-connections is magic. You realise there are no downsides – they keep us engaged with the world around us, keep our heads out of our phones and keep us connected to each other. Once I took a moment to appreciate this, I couldn't see a reason why I wouldn't keep doing it. I loved the energy afterwards, and loved the idea of bringing a little gift to someone else. You never know what people are going through on any given day, so a little kindness can go a long way.

HOW TO STOP APOLOGISING

Are you the sort of person who mumbles "Sorry!" when someone collides with you in the street, even when it's entirely their fault, or for not replying quickly enough to a text message, or in a restaurant when you've been brought the wrong order? If those scenarios sound uncomfortably familiar, you're not alone.

Saying "Sorry" too often is a common problem, especially among women. It's tattooed into our psyches that being nice equates to likability. While apologising is a powerful tool for building trust and improving social acceptance, overdoing it can diminish self-worth and self-confidence.

Apologising is usually born out of a desire to be respectful, but when it is done to excess it can become problematic. You may think you're presenting a kind and caring nature, but the message you're actually sending is that you lack confidence.

Repeatedly saying things such as, "Sorry I didn't get back to you straight away", or "Sorry, I look so awful; please excuse my hair", may reinforce the idea that you've done something wrong, when in actual fact you are apologising for just showing up as you are. This is detrimental to your confidence and can also lead to feeling unnecessary guilt and blaming yourself for things you don't need to. It's a vicious circle we want you to avoid.

Apologising when we *have* done something wrong is a real strength, and there is a skill to making a true apology. (We have released a podcast episode on it called "Heartfelt Apologies" if you want to learn more.)

But compulsive over-apologising presents itself as a weakness, and no one wants that. The bottom line is that over-apologising does not make you polite or agreeable or more likeable; instead, it minimises you, your presence and your contribution. In the process, you compromise your authentic self, gradually becoming less honest, less natural, and less "you". The outcome is that you will achieve the opposite of the approval that you seek, as others will respect you less and feel less at ease with you. At the same time, your own self-worth is diminished every time you blurt out "I'm sorry".

SELF-CARE STEPS TO STOP OVER-APOLOGISING

Step 1: Notice when you go to apologise

Bring awareness to how often you say sorry or feel compelled to do so. Make a list if you like.

Step 2: Before saying sorry, stop and question yourself

Ask yourself, *Have I actually done anything wrong here?* If the answer is no, then do not apologise! The urge can be easier to resist if you ask yourself the follow-up question: *If I didn't do something wrong, do I really want people to think or believe that I did?*

Step 3: Step into gratitude

The next time you feel an apology rising up inside you, think of a way to rephrase it into a statement of gratitude. For example, "I'm sorry I didn't get back to you sooner" could be replaced with "Thank you for your patience"; or, if a mistake is raised at work, instead of apologising you could try, "Thank you for pointing that out, I will rectify it."

Not only is this more pleasing to the other person, but it focuses your mind on positivity and abundance, which in turn helps you attract more positivity.

OUR EXPERIENCE

Lauren

Every woman I have ever attended in labour has apologised to me, their midwife or their partner. Often all of us. They range from "I'm sorry if my breath smells", "I'm sorry I didn't have time to wax my bikini line", "I'm sorry that I've kept you up all night", to "I'm sorry if I'm being loud",

"I'm sorry I keep asking you to rub my back, but it feels really good", "I'm sorry I was sick" and, my favourite, "I'm sorry, but I think I want an epidural". It is quite extraordinary. During one of the hardest and most vulnerable times in their life they are still saying sorry and worrying about everybody else. I am not an over-apologiser, but I am extremely British in the way that I will say sorry if someone bumps into me, and I have a deeply ingrained fear of being perceived as rude. As Nicole would say, it's an edge for me.

During this practice, I had to have a deeply uncomfortable conversation with a fellow school mum. I had not yet had a chance to meet her in person, which made it even harder to ring her up to talk to her about her son's screentime usage. My youngest son has an old hand-me-down iPad, which is linked to my phone and all calls ring into that. This little boy was calling to try and play with my son on their devices from the crack of dawn to late at night, endlessly. I had let it go for a few weeks, but it had now become a problem. Usually, a phone call of this nature would begin with me saying to the other mother something along the lines of "I'm so sorry for bothering you, I'm so sorry for calling, I'm so sorry to take up your time with this"; but on this occasion I wasn't sorry, as I had done nothing wrong. She, of course, had also not done anything wrong or even been aware of what was going on, so I made it very clear that I wasn't calling to have a go at her or sit in judgement on how she parents; I just needed to tell her what was going on. It was so hard not to apologise. But, as uncomfortable as it was, the call ended with us agreeing to arrange for our sons to have a playdate in the park.

Nicole

I used to have a client back in my hairdressing days whose first word to me was always "Sorry". She would apologise for anything and everything – being late or early, needing the toilet, being thirsty, and so on. This always struck me as sad; it was as if she was apologising for her mere existence. After researching the downsides of over-apologising, I felt curious going into this practice. I'm not an over-apologiser, but I was looking forward to seeing my response to this mental practice.

We did this practice back in Covid-19 days, and the government had just announced that on a certain date, hair and beauty salons could reopen. People hadn't had their hair cut in months and everyone wanted an appointment. My phone did not stop pinging.

It wasn't physically possible for me to reply to everyone immediately, and the texts did not let up. I found the whole experience overwhelming, so I turned my phone off. I just couldn't face it as it made me very anxious.

When I eventually found the courage and headspace to turn my phone back on, I took a deep breath and went through the texts one by one. And the first word I typed out was SORRY: "Sorry for taking so long to get back to you ..."

But no! I now had the tools to avoid this. I asked myself, Have I done anything wrong here? And if I haven't, do I want people to think I have? And do I want to communicate as if I have?

I regrouped, and the text began with "Thank you for your patience ..."

It felt uncomfortable, but right. Often, I find the easiest thing and the right thing are never the same.

WHAT DID WE LEARN?

Lauren

This week made me look at the times where I use "sorry" as a precursor to mitigate an uncomfortable conversation or situation. I can't be sure about whether my tendency to blurt out a "sorry" is because of my nationality, my sex or my conditioning but it made me reconsider when it is appropriate and heartfelt and when I am just using it as a disarming tool.

Nicole

When I looked at the nuances of "Am I sorry?", "Have I done anything wrong?" and "How can I respond in an affirming way?", I found it messy but revealing. Over-apologising is diminishing and not good for your sense of self. I love the reframe of gratitude – it makes your communication positive. Such a subtle shift will have a profound effect on your confidence.

HOW TO ASK FOR WHAT YOU WANT

What do you want?

This question can be filled with such fear. Yet it may possibly be the most important question we can ask ourselves. Because if you don't know what you want, if you don't allow space to understand what it is you want, if you don't give yourself permission to have what you want or even admit what you want, you will never have it. It's that simple.

And this will most likely lead to living a life by everyone else's needs and expectations – and who wants that?

> **Lauren:** *I've learnt not to answer when Nicole asks these questions. They are rhetorical. But the answer is no one. No one wants that.*

Women are so bad at stepping into what they want for themselves. The label that it's selfish or self-indulgent pops up again and again. We have been led to believe that, as women, we have to live for everyone else, doing what's expected and playing the role of the selfless, polite, good girl. So we feel guilty and undeserving for wanting, and we make excuses for not going after our desires – so much so that we sometimes struggle to even admit our truest desires to our nearest and dearest, and most of all to ourselves.

A scientific study testing gender told its subjects that they would be observed playing a word game and that they would be paid between US$3 and US$10 for participating. After each subject completed the task, an experimenter thanked the participant and said, "Here's $3. Is $3 okay?" For the men, it was not okay, and they said so. Their requests for more money exceeded those of the women by nine to one. Of the men, 23% requested more money, whereas of the women, only 3% asked for more, which was significant, especially as there were no gender differences in the outcome of the games.

So why are women less inclined to negotiate?

Women are less likely to negotiate for themselves for several reasons. First, they are often socialised from an early age not to promote their own interests and to focus instead on the needs of others. The messages girls receive from parents, teachers, other children, the media and society in general can be so powerful that when they become adults they may not realise they've internalised this behaviour; or they may realise it but not understand how it affects their willingness to negotiate. Women tend to assume that they will be recognised and rewarded for working hard and doing a good job. Unlike men, they haven't been taught that they can ask for more.

Women who actively pursue their own ambitions and promote their own interests may be labelled as "aggressive" or "pushy", whereas men may be labelled as simply "assertive". Women often don't get what they want and deserve, because society has made it difficult for us to simply ask for it.

WHY IS IT IMPORTANT TO ASK FOR WHAT YOU WANT?
The short and simple answer is: if you ask, you are more likely to get.

If you don't ask, you won't get. If you do ask, your chances immediately improve by 100%, and those are the kind of odds we like.

BENEFITS OF ASKING FOR WHAT YOU WANT
Asking clearly and politely for what you want:

- Can lead to you getting what you want
- Allows you to discover what you want
- Means you create a life on your own terms
- Will lead to you making better choices

SELF-CARE STEPS FOR ASKING FOR WHAT YOU WANT

Step 1: Ask yourself what you want
Question what it is that you really want. Write a list. Don't worry for now about the little gremlin on your shoulder telling you that you can't have it, we will deal with that later. For now, just bask in your desires. Trust your wants. Only when you're certain of your true desires will you have the courage and awareness to pursue them.

Step 2: Acknowledge the fear and step over it

Fear is an obstacle that blocks your capacity to receive. Have you ever thought that you might be afraid of actually getting what you want? Perhaps there is the fear of the responsibility that will come with that, or the fear of losing it, or the fear of what will happen if you ask but don't get. These are all common and valid, but they get in the way of you going after the things you yearn for most, so they need to be acknowledged and stepped over.

Step 3: Stop asking if you "deserve" what you want

Do not question whether or not you deserve things in life. We are here to remind you that you do. Think of us as two bossy Jewish mothers in your ear telling you that you do!

Step 4: Ask with trust

If you don't *believe* you're worthy, you will not be open to receiving. More often than not, you won't get what you want. Say to yourself, "I trust this is here, I trust I can have it, I trust that I want it – and that's enough."

Step 5: Ask without expectation

When you want something, you may be required to ask more than once, and try not to get too attached to the manner through which you receive it. If you want love, ask for it, but know that it might take a while and may not come from the partner you expect. If you want a fulfilling career, understand that you may get it, but perhaps not in the field, position or time frame you anticipate.

Step 6: Focus on the possibility

Focus on what asking will bring. This step is a game changer. This is your opportunity to ignore that gremlin we mentioned in Step 1. Push aside that nasty voice telling you that you can't have it or don't deserve it, and focus on the prize of getting what you want.

Step 7: If you don't ask, you don't get

We love this step so we saved it for last. Remember if you never ask for the things you want, you will never get them. Don't expect your partner to read your mind and know that you need a lie in and for them to get up with the kids. Ask for it and your chances improve by 100%.

Fun Fact

The worst that can happen after asking for what you want is that you stay where you are. You have nothing to lose by asking. It is just a question. Worst-case scenario is nothing changes, best-case scenario is everything does.

OUR EXPERIENCE

Lauren

I'm not that adept at asking for what I want. The thought of asking, not getting, and the resulting feeling of being let down and rejected having been vulnerable enough to have asked is too high a price to pay. So, as a general rule, I would rather just not ask. It is also wrapped up in being a mother to three children and automatically putting their needs before my own for the last 20 years.

The practice began when I had a realisation one evening about how reluctant I can be in asking for what I want. Most Friday nights I make roast chicken. I serve everyone else, always asking which part of the bird they would prefer. I have whatever is left at the end. Equally, if I'm invited to someone else's home, I will usually reply, "I don't mind," when I'm asked the same question. This particular evening, we had guests over and one of them was helping me serve. He asked me what I wanted, and without thinking, I answered, "The breast please." I immediately felt worried I was taking it away from someone else, then ashamed at myself for feeling guilty about simply voicing my preference. I shared this with Nicole on the podcast. She found it upsetting that I did not feel comfortable putting my own desires first. Ever since, she has taken it upon herself to always ask me for my preference when she makes a chicken and refuses to accept "I don't mind" as an answer!

When we were putting this book together, we were asked to submit a photo of ourselves for the back cover. When the proofs came back, I looked at it again and realised I really didn't like it. I struggled with whether or not to voice my feelings to Nicole. I didn't want to make a fuss or create more work. But because we have an honest, trusting relationship, and she is a person who believes in speaking up, I felt able to.

Without hesitation, she said we should choose another one, but it was harder to select the second time around. After 10 minutes or so of going through options, I said to Nicole that maybe we should just leave it as it is as I didn't want to come across like a diva by asking to swap it.

Nicole turned from the computer screen to face me. "This is your book," she said. "It's going to be out there forever. Why should you compromise on having an image of yourself that you're not happy with? You should have something that you want, not settle for something that you don't like." She was absolutely right, but I needed that reminder. We found a substitution that we both liked and submitted it.

Since we did this practice, I have been trying harder to ask for what I want more often and have found a natural progression into figuring out what I want without always having to consider everyone else's needs, or presuming that my own needs are less important and have to come last.

Nicole

I was excited to put this practice to the test. I felt very ready to break down that self-built brick wall that asking for too much meant I was somehow unlikeable.

Around the same time, we were testing out an exercise mirror for the show. It's full length and you type in any exercise class you want to do and the instructor appears in the mirror and guides you through the workout. It is a very cool product and it retails for around £2,000. Lauren and I were both lucky enough to be gifted one each to try out for the show. While I felt lucky, Lauren was less than pleased to have a machine in her bedroom reminding her to exercise. I think her words were, "It's watching me."

Just before we were set to record an interview with the founder of the company, I mentioned to Lauren and our podcast engineer James how I wanted a mirror as a giveaway for one lucky listener. My initial thought was that there is no way she was going to gift us a third mirror. After much debate among the three of us, James kindly said he would ask her.

As the interview was drawing to a close, I was subconsciously willing James to ask her about the giveaway, but the words were not coming out of his mouth. So, I stepped in to that uncomfortable place, got brave and made the request myself. The founder replied with, "Okay, sure." That was it. I asked, she responded, and I got what I wanted simply because I asked for it. All I had to do was get out of my comfort zone, away from the narrative that I mustn't ask, and suddenly I stepped into a huge possibility. That was quite the lesson.

After that, my "asking for what I wanted juices" flowed and it became a transformational week.

Would you like to write an article about us in your newspaper? Yes
Will you be a guest on the show? Yes
Can we come to your retreat for free? Yes
Can we have a meeting to discuss our daughter? Yes
Can you send us more CBD? Yes

At the end of the week, I noticed a feature on the Apple podcast front page called *Spotlight*. This is where they push one show for a whole month. So, I wrote to Apple to enquire if we could be considered for the placement. This one was a bold ask, but this was the point.

I got a response a week or so later saying thank you for enquiring about the promotion … but there was no definitive answer, no guidance in how we could go about it. So, in this case, I didn't get what I wanted BUT – and this is key – my life was still the same, nothing bad happened. No need for any fear. Again, life-changing.

WHAT DID WE LEARN?

Lauren

I have chosen to share my life with a romantic partner and a work partner who are more comfortable in standing up for themselves and asking for their needs to be met than I am. I do feel inspired by that, but it also means they often do the work for me. I need to spend a little more time getting uncomfortable and vulnerable by flexing my own muscles in getting what I want and feeling like I deserve it, rather than allowing them to fight my corner. My mantra moving forwards is: *It's okay to ask and, if you do ask, the answer might actually be yes.*

Nicole

This has been the most life-changing practice for me. Realising that the worst that can happen by asking for what I want is staying where I am has left me with much more courage to step in and ask. I now focus on the *possibility rather than the narrative of being "too much". We want what we want because we want it, and our desires are there because it's what we desire. It's that simple. The shame or embarrassment we feel about it is from societal messaging that women cannot and must not be too much. In order for us to be happy we have to know what we want and ask for it.*

Nothing ventured, nothing gained.

TAKE-AWAY TIPS

Micro-connections
Connecting with others, even for a brief moment, lifts your mood as well as the other person's. Think of it as a small act of kindness with benefits for you too. You don't have to go out of your way to engage, and once you start to strengthen that social muscle you may find it becomes an automatic part of your day.

Over-apologising
Rephrasing an apology into a statement of gratitude is going to improve your self-esteem and is a more positive and affirming way to move through the world.

Asking for what you want
Focus on the possibility of getting what you want and remember, even if the answer is no, you will never be worse off. You have everything to gain and nothing to lose. It's win-win.

READER CHALLENGES

Lauren's challenge
Inspired by the work of Professor Barbara Fredrickson, try making three micro-connections a day.

Nicole's challenge
Write down or make a mental list of what you truly want, what desires live in your heart and then ask for it. That's the tricky bit, but that's also where all the fun lives. Allow yourself to have what you want.

4

Calm

More often than not, navigating life's daily complexities can leave us feeling stressed, anxious and overwhelmed. The pressure placed upon us by society is immense. We are expected to do and be everything and everywhere.

As women, society tells us to be independent, but not "left on the shelf"; to be strong, but not aggressive; to settle down and have a family, but all the while having a successful and fulfilling career. To go on lavish holidays, curate the perfect home, to be attractive, to have a nine-step skin care routine, to be a certain size, to fight for social justice, to be responsible; oh and to floss. We have to keep up with the latest fashions, TikTok trends and celebrity gossip. To be able to instantly reply to every email, WhatsApp and text. Unsurprisingly, this pressure has brought us to the point of complete exhaustion. The need for calm and inner peace is essential.

ANXIETY OVERLOAD

In the UK, a little over 1 in 10 of us will be living with an anxiety disorder at any one time – that's over 8 million people. In any given week in England, 6 in 100 people will be diagnosed with generalised anxiety disorder (GAD). We are at a point where, sadly, we have to teach ourselves the most fundamental practices of wellbeing, like breathing.

So, writing a chapter on calm felt key to the book, as it is the antidote to all of this chaos we surround ourselves with. This chapter focuses on how to bring that illustrious peace into our everyday lives. Keeping a calm mind, especially in times of crisis, is a superpower, which will help you to navigate your life with more balance and harmony. Think of this as your little toolbox of tranquillity. Namaste.

If you can overcome your mind, you can overcome almost anything. And by "overcome", we mean being able to effectively control your emotional responses to life's unexpected tests – because most of your deepest pain and frustration on a daily basis will come from the way you respond, not the way life is. As Buddha said:

Pain in life is inevitable
Suffering is not
Pain is what the world does to you
Suffering is what you do to yourself
Pain is inevitable
Suffering is optional
                    Buddha

However, as Zen as Buddha was, he wasn't receiving targeted ads to tell him that he should be buying shapewear.

There's a plethora of scientific evidence that tells us our brain simply works better when it's relaxed. The limbic (or emotional) brain is like a "router" for incoming information. When we're stressed, information is passed to our unconscious mind, and we automatically react. However, when we are calm, our amygdala and hippocampus feed this sensory information through our "higher" executive brain, allowing us to think and behave in a calm and rational manner instead. The upshot is, even if you're staring down the barrel of a genuine crisis, the best option is always to cultivate calm.

BENEFITS OF CALM

When you take the time to cultivate calm:

- You feel more in control of your emotions and your life
- You think more clearly
- You can discuss problems with ease and certainty
- You *respond* rather than *react*
- You are more creative
- Your concentration improves
- Your digestion improves
- Your blood pressure improves
- Your relationships improve
- You have more compassion

THE PRACTICES

- **Cold showers**
- **Breathwork**
- **Singing to the land**

Beyond the practices we will cover in this chapter, there are many ways to find calm, including:

- Meditation*
- Self-compassion*
- Being in nature, tree hugging, awe walking (see Chapter 6)*
- EFT (Emotional Freedom Technique)*
- Sleep
- Classical music*
- Laughter yoga*
- Sophrology*

- Weighted blankets*
- Grounding*
- Mindfulness
- Yoga
- Eating more whole foods
- Socialising
- Reading
- Reducing your caffeine intake

*The suggestions with an asterisk are the practices we have released podcast episodes on. Feel free to have a listen and learn more. Just search for Self Care Club wherever you get your podcasts and scroll down for the episode.

While we hope that the practices in this chapter will help to ease and manage your anxiety, you may still find yourself in need of professional help. There are plenty of effective treatment methods, including talking therapies and medication. Anxiety, when left untreated, can become debilitating and interfere with daily functioning. If you feel this is something that resonates with you, we encourage you to find support. Please see the back of this book for suggested places where you can reach out.

54321 sense check

Before we dive into the practices, we wanted to highlight a technique called the "54321 sense check". The practice is fast and effective, and a good tool to have in your back pocket when you feel anxiety is washing over you like a tsunami. This is something you can try as a circuit breaker.

When we are experiencing overwhelming anxiety, the one thing that happens to us all is that we are pulled out of the present moment. Our mind and thoughts race and we conjure up a barrage of terrifying what-ifs and outcomes that are based in the past or the future. The 54321 technique helps you to physically reconnect to the present through your body. It grounds you and plants you back to earth. Your mind can take you deep into the darkest of fears, but your body can only ever be right here in the present. If you are having an acute moment, here is how to do it.

Step 1: Become aware of your breath
Slow your breathing by taking three long, deep breaths and become aware of your environment.

Step 2: Notice 5 objects
For example, notice the plant on the table, or the glass of water in front of you. Take your time and really focus on exactly what your eyes are seeing.

Step 3: Become aware of 4 things you can touch
For example, the texture of your denim jeans, the smooth wood of the chair you are sitting in, the softness of your hair. Touch these things if you want to.

Step 4: Become aware of 3 things you can hear
For example, traffic, people talking, the hum of a washing machine.

Step 5: Become aware of 2 things you can smell
Is there a smell in the air around you, perhaps the smell of your own perfume, your skin, your clothes?

Step 6: Become aware of 1 thing you can taste
Did you have coffee earlier? Maybe you can still taste the flavour in your mouth. Do you have a piece of gum or a mint to hand?

Repeat this six-step process as many times as necessary until you feel calmer. You can try it out any time your mind is taking you away from the present moment; reconnect with your senses to bring yourself back into your body and back to the present.

COLD SHOWERS

Over the past few years there has been an enormous rise in the popularity of cold-water therapy, with many people going out of their way to turn themselves into human ice lollies all in the name of wellness. Whether it's wild swimming, ice baths, cold plunge pools or following the teachings of Wim Hof, people are really leaning into the concept of cold.

But why on earth would you swap your lovely, warm shower for a freezing one?

BENEFITS OF COLD SHOWERS
Cold showers have been proven to:

- **Boost your immune system**. Ongoing stress may increase inflammation, which can then lead to a cycle of inflammation-induced illnesses and anxiety.
- **Help improve blood circulation**. When you cool down your body temperature, your system responds by moving blood. Anxiety may raise blood pressure, so, in theory, a cold shower may help lower it and lower your heart rate by up to 15%.
- **Offer relief for symptoms of depression**. Cold showers stimulate what is known as "the blue spot", which is the brain's primary source of noradrenaline. The mild electroshock delivered to the brain by the cold shower sends an overwhelming number of electrical impulses from peripheral nerve endings to the brain, which could result in an anti-depressive effect. One study reviewed the role of cold showers in the treatment of depression. Participants experienced an improvement in their symptoms after several weeks of two- to three-minute sessions of cold-water showers at 68°F (20°C), once or twice a day.
- **Act as a circuit breaker**. This is especially helpful if you suffer from panic attacks. The shock of a cold shower can temporarily take your mind off the things you are anxious about. The few minutes you are focusing on coping with the sensation of the cold on your body may act as a mindfulness practice.

Unfun Fact

Cold showers may not be a good idea if you're unwell. For some people, initially, the temperature might be too hard on your immune system, so it's best to ease into the cooler temperatures. It could also be troublesome for someone already prone to heart arrhythmia or anyone with heart issues. So, if you have high blood pressure or any heart condition, we suggest always consulting your doctor before trying a cold shower.

SELF-CARE STEPS FOR COLD SHOWERS

Step 1: Start hot, but end cold
Take your shower as normal, but finish off with at least 30–60 seconds of cold water. If you liked the sensation, do it again the next day and see how two days in a row makes you feel. It may help to start with putting your arms and legs in before fully stepping under the shower head.

Step 2: Listen to your body and its response
You shouldn't step out of the shower and be in a state where you can't stop shivering, as that means your cold exposure was too long. You'll quickly notice that you are able to tolerate the cold more and more until eventually it becomes something you may actually look forward to.

Step 3: Don't be too serious about it
Make it fun, for example, one woman we know combines her cold showers with her daily squats. If it's going to stress you out, then it's not worth it. This is supposed to improve your life, not scare you to death!

OUR EXPERIENCE

Lauren
I was both furious and curious in equal measure. It felt like a classic one of Nicole's punishments disguised as podcast practices. I'm so averse to cold water, and I would never drink water with ice – that horrible feeling of the cold sliding down my throat making your insides feel icy, bleurgh! I like things as hot as possible. You could brew a cup of tea in my scalding bath water.

It seemed like this was going to be something I needed to psych myself up to do. The best method seemed to be to get straight out of bed and directly into the shower – getting it done before your brain has even registered that you're awake.

My method was to start tepid, wash my body, shampoo and rinse my hair, then put conditioner in and start to lower the temperature very slowly and rinse off in the cold. Every day I showered (which, for me, is not every day), I made it a little colder. What I noticed immediately was that my hair was shinier, easier to dry and more manageable – that was a bonus. I also noticed my face looked quite fresh, and there was no puffiness.

As the week went on, I began to lose the fear as it became a known entity. I wouldn't say that I looked forward to it, but there was a degree of mental achievement that I had done it; it also builds mental resilience, which is something I love. It became a dare – a fun, sick, masochistic game I could play.

Nicole

I had tried cold showers many times before; I was far from Wim Hof, but the week wasn't going to be a stretch. (Lauren gets annoyed when I'm not finding a practice difficult.)

To begin with, I got out of the shower forgetting it was cold shower week, so I got back in because I am committed to the cause and turned the faucet to cold. I managed 22 seconds and emerged feeling exhilarated. It was difficult and unpleasant, yet lovely all at the same time. My body was tingly for a while after and I felt great. I'll admit I was a bit of a coward as I refused to put my head under.

The next day, I couldn't wait to turn the shower to cold. My target was to beat my time from the day before. Yep, it's always a game and having that personal competitive element makes it much more fun.

Lauren: *Eye roll*

From then on, I had a cold shower every day, and slowly increased my time daily.

I managed 40 seconds by the end of the week. Obviously, I am still trying to beat that time.

WHAT DID WE LEARN?

Lauren

If you do it first thing, it feels like you have achieved something before the day has even begun. It turned out to be quite a fun experience and on the physical side, my hair looked better. However, I was disappointed to lose my "shower thinking time". I couldn't process stuff and have those creative meditative moments that I usually enjoy.

I learnt that I am capable of hard things and that I can do more than I give myself credit for. It's all about building willpower and self-discipline – both of which I could do with improving.

Nicole

The sensation of my body trying to regulate itself became totally addictive, and that gradual post-shower rebalancing is exhilarating. I love anything that pushes me out of my comfort zone, and cold-water immersion does exactly that.

This started out as a physical challenge, but it quickly revealed its many mental benefits. It brings resilience and inner strength, which are two things I am always striving for. This practice is self-care personified.

BREATHWORK

Let's kick off with a grounding thought: no matter what is happening around you or what life may be chucking your way, you always have access to your breath.

Although breathwork is very on trend right now, it's far from new. It has been a modality for centuries in Buddhism, yoga and t'ai chi; and it's only since the 1960s that it became popular in the western world.

Breathwork refers to any type of breathing exercises or techniques. Your breath brings oxygen into your body so that you can live and thrive. Physical and emotional stress affects how you breathe. When you feel stressed, your breath tends to become fast and shallow. This limits the oxygen entering your bloodstream. Your brain tells your body that there is a threat, and your body responds in fight or flight.

Your stress response gets turned on automatically, but very few of us know how to calm this system down. When you take time to slow down and purposefully breathe deeply and slowly, you tell your brain that everything is okay. Your brain communicates to your body that it's safe to relax. The fight-or-flight response decreases, and your body can begin to function normally.

There are many forms of breathwork therapy that involve breathing in a conscious and systematic way, and many people find it assists with deep relaxation or leaves them feeling energised. Some practices are vigorous; others are led by how the body wants to breathe. Whatever the breathing technique – be it box breathing, circular, breath of fire, nostril breathing, opposite nostril breathing, mouth breathing, breath holding – the healing mechanism remains the same: the mind-body connection.

Stress is bad for the brain and research has repeatedly shown that learning to relax is one of the most important keys to long-term health and vitality. Being able to deeply relax will stimulate your vagus nerve.

Lauren: *And we all know what happens in vagus stays in vagus.*

The vagus nerve connects to all the body's immune cells, stem cells, organs and tissues; and it has the ability to turn off your stress response and activate your relaxation response, making it incredibly healing to the nervous system. Breathwork is one of the most powerful tools we have to activate the vagus nerve and improve the brain and mind-body connection.

BENEFITS OF BREATHWORK

Using breathwork as part of you daily routine can:

- Stimulate the parasympathetic nerve that calms your body
- Balance out blood pressure
- Allow you to sleep deeply
- Give you energy
- Stop negative thinking
- Help you to shift embedded thoughts or thought patterns, which helps you to break a habit
- Strengthen respiratory function
- Improve your immune system
- Release stress hormones from your body
- Reduce feelings of depression and anxiety
- Improve mental focus
- Decrease addictive behaviours

SELF-CARE STEPS FOR BREATHWORK

Step 1: Allow yourself to breathe

Intentionally gift yourself a few minutes to practise breathwork. (Yes, it is a gift.)

Step 2: Pick the type of breathing exercise you want to engage in

You can choose from the options below, or find your own rhythm of breath that works for you.

Step 3: Sit upright or lie down

If you are new to breathwork you may experience slight dizziness or lightheadedness, or some tingling in your fingers and toes so sitting or lying down is advised plus it is more relaxing. Sit upright to expand your diaphragm and lung capacity. Make your environment comfortable.

Step 4: Close your eyes

And breathe ...

Please remember there are many ways to breathe, and we encourage you to find your own flow of breath. With that said, here are a few suggestions to kickstart you into a breathing Buddha.

DIAPHRAGMATIC BREATHING

1. Place one hand on your chest and the other hand on your abdomen.
2. Inhale through your nose for four beats, feeling your abdomen expand. (You may feel slight tension the first few times you inhale.) Only the lower hand should move; the top hand should remain still.
3. Hold your breath for two beats.
4. Exhale very slowly and steadily through your mouth for six beats. The mouth and jaw should be relaxed.
5. Repeat.

Fun Fact

You can use the hand placement of diaphragmatic breathing with any of the breathwork practices below.

BOX BREATHING

Box breathing, also known as square breathing, is a technique used when taking slow, deep breaths. It's also called four-square breathing. This technique is beneficial to anyone, anywhere.

1. Breathe in through your nose for four beats.
2. Hold your breath for four beats.
3. Exhale for four beats.
4. Repeat for three to four rounds until you feel centred.

4-7-8

This technique is similar to box breathing, but the count differs.

1. Breathe in for four beats.
2. Hold your breath for seven beats.
3. Exhale for eight beats. A longer exhale encourages you to completely empty your lungs.

7/11 OR ZEN BREATHING

This technique involves you breathing in through the nostrils and slowly breathing out through slightly pursed lips, creating airflow resistance, so that the exhalation lasts two to three times longer than inhalation.

1. Sit in an upright position to allow for maximum lung expansion.
2. Breathe in for seven beats.
3. Purse your lips to the size of a pea.
4. Breathe out for 11 beats.
5. Try to focus on your diaphragm and abdominal muscles.
6. Repeat until you feel calm.

You may prefer to breathe in for a count of three and out for five; the numbers are arbitrary as the premise of this practice is for the outbreath to be longer than the inbreath.

OUR EXPERIENCE

Lauren

I have been teaching breathwork in my capacity as a doula for 16 years. I felt like I had spent a lot of time focusing on breathwork for others, but never for myself, so I was interested to see how it would go. I was also fascinated to see if Nicole would actually be able to sit still and breathe or if she would multi-task and do it while she was loading the washing machine.

I started with a couple of simple, quick exercises for morning and evening. I decided to spend the five minutes between my alarm going off and actually getting up to do the practice. I usually spend this time patting the dog who is asleep on top of me and thinking about which bits of me are stiff and how much I don't want to get up, so this was a refreshing change. As the week progressed, I found that I felt better equipped for whatever the day was going to chuck at me; almost as if I was coming at it already armed. I couldn't pinpoint exactly if I felt more energised, more relaxed or just in a better mood – but I definitely felt a little more prepared.

In the evenings, I normally get into bed, read my book and then, once I feel tired, I'm out like a light. This week I lay down, started to do my breathwork practice, felt a bit bored, then always fell asleep before getting to the end of the five minutes of breathing. It didn't serve me as well as the morning practice, but I can imagine that it would relax anyone who struggles with sleep or anxious thoughts at night.

On the last day of the practice week, I went to a postnatal meeting with a client and we reminisced about a very uncomfortable 40 minutes spent standing in a horrendously brightly lit fluorescent corridor at 3am, along with a number of other women, waiting to be seen. There could have been panic in that situation as she was having long, strong contractions every two minutes and there were no medics available. The only tool I had in my toolbox to assist her was her breath. I coached her through every contraction. It was all she had, and it was all she needed.

Nicole

Sorry to start this lovely tranquil practise with a moan but here we are. I felt like a bit of an idiot having to be "taught" how to breathe. Breathing is the most fundamental thing we do all day, every day, and now I am being schooled on it.

Nevertheless, breathwork week came at a perfect time as I had a huge race at the end of the week. I had been training for six long months, and to say I was nervous would be a vast understatement. Breathwork was needed.

Not being one to sit still or waste time, I decided to practise my breathing while I cooked my daily porridge. The fact I felt I had to be doing something else while breathing was a concern in itself. I fully committed for two mornings, but nothing much happened apart from a bowl of cooked porridge.

By day three, I felt the two minutes could be better utilised and I decided to put a wash on, cook porridge and do breathwork all at the same time – now that was what I called productive.

I know what you're thinking: that was not anything like practising breathwork, and, yes, I was aware of it. I felt unimpressed with myself.

After failing miserably, I needed to give it another go and as I clearly couldn't behave myself during the day I felt it best to try again in bed – the less distractions the better.

I lay in bed, hand on tummy, breathed in for four and out for four and felt my stomach rising and falling. I fell asleep peacefully and without a screen. #winning

Race day. I wasn't racing until 6:30pm, and I made a pact with myself in the morning not to waste any nervous energy. The race itself was so physically demanding that I needed to conserve as much energy as I could. Every time I felt nervous energy rise in me, I used the box breathing technique. What probably would've been a day filled with anxiety and stress turned out to be fun and exciting, and I truly believe it was breathwork that kept me centred and calm.

WHAT DID WE LEARN?
Lauren
This week was a good reminder for me to not always associate breathwork with pain. Because I have used it for so long as a technique to help women cope with labour pain rather than using it as a relaxation tool, I had to rebrand it in my head. This week taught me to repurpose it for myself and to use it in a way to add value to my life.

Nicole
No matter what is happening, you always have your breath, it is always available to you and sometimes it may be the only thing available to you, unwavering and loyal to a fault.

This week taught me that being intentional with my breathing is full of advantages. It aids me in every stage of wake and sleep. While my heart rate is pumping through the roof in the gym, during my everyday activities and to calm me. It's magic. I very much struggle to slow down, but if I allow the space to breathe I could bring a lot more calm into my life.

SINGING TO THE LAND

Singing to the land is a ceremony that allows us to connect to Mother Earth and cultivate calm by being at one with nature. Ceremonies like this are the sacred seeds of healing and nourishment with the Earth, and can help bring balance where it is needed. We had the privilege of trying this practice on a retreat in the awe-inspiring landscape of the Welsh valleys. The best way to give you an idea of what it's about is to jump straight into our experiences.

OUR EXPERIENCE

Lauren

I was woken at 6am by Charlotte Church singing an aria outside my bedroom door. Let's just all agree – that's not normal. Nicole remains adamant that I am the only person on earth who has muttered "shut up" to the woman globally regarded as having the voice of an angel.

By 6.30am, still half asleep, I was outside in a field for "celestial blessings", which turned out to be the retreat's name for what is more commonly known as a silent disco. While watching Charlotte and the other residents excitedly don headphones and scatter like sheep to get their groove on among the hedgerows, I did what felt most natural to me … immediately fled the grounds. I headed down the narrow lanes towards the local village before realising I had no idea how far away it was or where I was going, no phone signal and no money. I regretfully concluded that I had no option but to turn back. On my return, while being aurally violated by Gloria Estefan's "Rhythm is Gonna Get You", I came upon a sheep who had managed to get its head stuck through a fence. After rescuing it and awarding myself the title of "amateur vet of the year 2023", I regretfully returned to the retreat.

The disco was immediately followed by "morning gathering", which I naively thought might be a coffee and a croissant, but turned out to be a stealth therapy session consisting of a talking and listening exercise that I had to perform in partnership with a fellow resident, a woman I had only met the day before. As she shared her innermost feelings and cried, I sat looking at her with what I hoped was a kind and empathetic expression and prayed for it to be over soon. I was yet to have breakfast and was already physically and emotionally spent having dealt with emergency animal rescue, 1990s pop, and being forced to conjure up and express my feelings to a stranger without so much as a cup of tea in me all before 9am. I was grumpy, tired and, at this point, questioning my life choices.

At 10am it was time for the main attraction of the three-day retreat: Singing to the Land. The premise was, as far as we were aware, going in to the forest with Charlotte Church to commune with the land and express yourself through singing. We gathered in a forest clearing – majestic pines towering above us and the sound of a waterfall as our backdrop. Charlotte led us through a warm-up exercise. We were then instructed to think of a tune and hum it to ourselves as we walked the land for 15 minutes until we were called back by her werewolf howl. I stomped off and, despite it being mid-April, the only tune that repeated in my head was "We Wish You a Merry Christmas". After a few rounds of muttering the song under my breath, my instincts told me that this was quite clearly not for me and I needed to immediately remove myself from this situation. So, for the second time that morning, I decided to make a run for it. I made my way out of the forest, round the house and back down the lane. I passed a farmer but noted he was on a one-seater tractor and therefore no good as an escape vehicle. With no sign of civilisation in sight and driven by curiosity and the fear of Nicole's wrath, I eventually turned round and retraced my steps. I could hear Charlotte's werewolf calling me back and, knowing I had been longer than the time allotted to me, I howled in return to acknowledge I was heading back. After all, how bad could it be?

I returned to the group – Nicole gave me a look that said a thousand words – just as they were heading to the darkest part of the forest for the second part of the session. Charlotte began to speak in a foreign tongue. I momentarily wondered if it was Welsh, but she explained that we were now going to learn to speak in our "creature language". The task was to make up a language, to allow the words and sounds to flow through you and speak it to yourself, getting used to the feeling of this imaginary vocabulary, and then to add a harmony to it so you were effectively singing nonsense to yourself. WTAF? It was at this juncture I started to feel as if I was unravelling. Having arrived at the retreat as a perfectly sane, steady, well-adjusted, middle-aged woman, I was now being encouraged to behave like an escaped asylum patient (in pink wellies).

I had reached breaking point. Having expressed my feelings about this in full to Nicole and a worried-looking fellow resident, I stomped off for the third and final time that morning. Marching through the undergrowth, muttering under my breath (in English), I saw Charlotte perched on a tree stump, her beautiful voice carrying through the air, and marched straight past her until the wolf howl called me back to our last meeting point.

We stood in the woods in a circle, and Charlotte stood like a radiant woodland nymph with bare feet, a flowing skirt, an open beaming smile and her shawl scattered with fallen leaves. She warmly invited us to feedback on how the session had been for us. While others opened up about the discovery of their creature language and sharing their vocal offerings to the hills, I stood in stony silence until it was my turn. We looked at each other across the glade. "Wow," said Charlotte to me, "You're absolutely fuming. How did that make you feel?" "Unhinged," I replied.

Nicole

I had been wanting to "sing to the land with Charlotte Church" for months, ever since I read about it in the Sunday Times. All winter, I had been imagining myself sat on the hills of the glorious Welsh countryside, the sun on my face, Charlotte sat by my side singing to the birds while I soaked in the moment. A private concert if you will.

When we started at 10am and made our way into the woods, my fantasy was coming to life. We reached a beautiful place in the forest. The trees felt enclosed and majestic and the waterfall ran down into the stream beside us. Charlotte invited us to gather in a circle. I felt excited and calm in equal measure. Charlotte was about to release her angelic voice to Mother Earth and I couldn't have felt more alive. As I glanced over to Lauren to share this momentous occasion, her vibe was less warrior-of-the-woods and more moody-teenager-meets-Craig-Revel-Horwood. I ignored it.

The circle was formed by eight women and Charlotte took us through some vocal warm-ups. She instructed us to hum notes from high to low and vice versa. As it turns out, singing in front of Charlotte Church in the middle of the woods didn't feel as organic as I'd imagined; unsurprisingly, I got stage fright. In truth, the last thing I needed was to listen to seven other women finding their vocal range when all I'd really come for was to listen to Charlotte.

Luckily, the warm-up was brief. I planted my feet into the ground, closed my eyes and opened my ears ready to hear Charlotte break into "Amazing Grace", or whatever song she had chosen for this magical moment, when she said in her recognisable Welsh accent, "Right. Off you go, go walk and sing to the land. Whatever comes, just let it guide you, and I will call you back in 15 minutes."

What? I didn't want to hear myself sing, or the other seven participants for that matter, I was there to hear HER sing. As if everyone expected this, they all dispersed into the woods. I was fixated on Charlotte, so I followed her deep into the woods, wanting to catch any snippet of sound that may come from her. When she turned round and saw me, I suddenly realised how creepy I must've seemed. I quickly scurried away in the opposite direction, mortified.

Nevertheless, I was still so transfixed on hearing Charlotte's voice that I hid behind a tree and fell silent to see if I could hear her. I couldn't, so I pulled myself together and began the exercise as it was intended and tried to let go of my disappointment. I hummed "Moon River" over and over and over and over again, trying to delete from my mind the shame of following Charlotte into the woods.

Moments later she wolf-howled us back to the meeting point; I was the first one back, which didn't help my fangirl paranoia. Lauren was nowhere to be fucking seen. We gathered and waited and still, no Lauren. After about 10 minutes Charlotte gave up on whether Lauren was going to reappear, and led us to a deeper and darker part of the woods. Still no Lauren. We carried on walking, and then Lauren appeared, looking furious. It definitely was not the look of someone who had just been connecting with Mother Earth, but I was too busy obsessing about Charlotte's potential singing to give her any notice.

It was time for stage two of singing to the land. We had reached the oldest oak tree in the wood named Bryn. I wanted to ask who named him, but after "stalking-gate" I felt it best to stay under the radar. We walked round Bryn to pay tribute to him, then took a seat.

I thought, this was the moment: Charlotte was going to sing. She had been waiting for the perfect setting. I was ready for "Hallelujah", but what came out of her voice was her harmonised "creature language". To be fair to Charlotte, it still sounded like velvet, she could sing the dictionary and sound phenomenal, but my expectations were trashed for the second time that morning.

We were told to go off and speak and sing in our own creature language, and the group dispersed for the second time. You'll be relieved to know I composed myself and stood still till Charlotte was out of sight.

I spotted Lauren by a tree. Her hat was askew, her jeans were muddy and she was spiralling. That swiftly turned to venting and then screaming, as if everything was somehow my fault. I tried to calm her down, but she stormed off again telling me she was going. I didn't know if she meant going mad or going home, but I was pretty sure that she wasn't going to explore her creature language.

I gave up with the intended exercise at this point (sorry not sorry, Charlotte) but what with the stalking saga, the disappointment of no actual singing and now Lauren throwing a tantrum, I was over it.

We gathered for the final time a few minutes later, and hummed together "Amazing Grace". Well, I didn't hum, I just listened. It wasn't quite what I had originally hoped, but it was magical nonetheless. And I decided there and then, when Charlotte does another concert, I'll be getting tickets.

WHAT DID WE LEARN?
Lauren
I think the less said, the better.

Nicole
I learnt that I am more open-minded than Lauren, and that there is such a thing as "creature language".

TAKE-AWAY TIPS

Cold showers

No one else is going to push you into that shower – you just have to take the plunge. Each time you do it, it will get easier. To be the best version of yourself, you have to step outside of your comfort zone. The thought of taking cold showers every day may be just as daunting as making any other lifestyle change, but you can overcome this, by turning it into an experiment.

This is where our practices merge: use breathwork to help you fight the cold water. Challenge yourself, and try to increase the length of the shower every time you do it; even if you only manage an extra second, it makes it fun and gives you a sense of achievement.

Breathwork

No matter what is going on in your life or in your head, your breath is always available to you – so make sure you use it to bring something positive. You will never feel worse for having taken a moment to breathe.

READER CHALLENGES

Lauren's challenge
Even if you are, like me, someone who loves hot baths and showers, step out of your comfort zone and commit to trying out cold showers for five days. See what benefits it brings you.

Nicole's challenge
Put aside five minutes a day to breathe. If five minutes feels easy, make it ten minutes. Let your breath support you in your everyday life.

Bonus challenge
Hug a tree and sing it a song – you may feel silly, but also totally invigorated.

Calm at home

Let's take a look at practical ways to help you organise your external environment to create more internal calm.

Tidying up

We are a product of our environment, so, if we surround ourselves with mess and clutter, then our mind will feel exactly that. This is why tidying methods (for example, those promoted by Marie Kondo in her hit Netflix show) and minimalism trends have become so prevalent in recent years. According to a study, having a lot of visual stimuli present when trying to concentrate on one stimulus will result in those other items competing for your attention. Put simply, if there's too much going on in your view, you will need to concentrate harder to get a task done. Aesthetically pleasing and ordered environments are balm to a frazzled soul.

The benefits of tidying up include:

- Space saving: creates room to breathe, rest and relax
- Time saving: less items around means less to tidy up and more free time
- Money saving: uncovers forgotten, useful items you already own, removing the need to buy more; or you can sell any unwanted items

Minimalism

Minimalism teaches us how to declutter our lives as a whole. At its core, it's about living a deliberate and intentional life, free from excess and distractions. That includes general consumerism, tech consumption, social interactions, thoughts and behaviours.

For example, beyond minimising your material possessions, you must also shed the negative stories you tell yourself and reduce the influx of WhatsApps, emails and social media notifications.

It's about looking at and assessing your priorities so that you can discard the things that don't bring value to your life. Anything physical, digital, mental or emotional that gets in the way of achieving your goals and living a fulfilling life needs to be looked at, slimmed down or edited out. Minimalism can assist you in stepping into tasks such as editing your friendships and only make plans with people you actually want to spend your limited and precious time with. It can also help you to think about your mental clutter – for example, any fears that keep you from moving forward.

Minimalism reduces clutter and simplifies your life, which can lead to less stress and a clearer mind. Embracing minimalism can:

- Save money
- Improve mental health
- Help the environment
- Improve focus
- Improve creativity

Tips to help you embrace minimalism

- **Delete apps on your phone that you don't use.** This is a quick and easy introduction to minimalism, and will get you into the habit of seeing things disappear. It's low risk and high reward.
- **Turn off social media notifications.** You do not need to be informed every time someone likes your post. If you need that validation multiple times throughout your day, then it might be time to look at why.

- **Clean up your communication and social media**. Delete messages, emails and WhatsApp groups for birthday parties or events that have finished. Unfollow people on social media and delete old contacts in your phone. Unsubscribe from email spam.
- **Chuck/donate one thing away a day**. By the end of the year you will have gotten rid of 365 items that you didn't need.
- **Put it in the basket, but don't check out**. When online shopping you can get the dopamine high by just going as far as selecting an item, without the clutter or spending the money.
- **Think about what you are buying someone**. When you are shopping for presents, consider whether your choice is truly a gift or are you just giving them more responsibility and clutter.

Decluttering

Decluttering is the process of putting the miscellaneous physical things around you away where they belong. It is a form of self-care that isn't talked about much, but decluttering can actually be one of the most effective ways of helping clear your mind so that you can feel happier and less burdened by all the physical stuff.

Scientific studies have shown that there is a direct relationship between clutter and stress. Clutter can take up your time, space and energy, and it can steal your peace. Living in a cluttered space is associated with reduced productivity and chronic procrastination, as well as a depressed mood, higher cortisol levels and a decrease in satisfaction with life among older adults.

More often than not, we don't realise how emotionally weighed down our stuff makes us feel until we start letting it go. Your home should be the ultimate place for relaxation. Clutter interferes with that. Too much stuff to deal with can make you feel overwhelmed and as if you have a never-ending to-do list. Remove the clutter and your space takes on a different energy.

Once you begin the process of decluttering, you are very unlikely to miss anything you have discarded; instead, you may experience a sense of relief and lightness. And, once clear, you are in a position to surround yourself with things that you genuinely want, need, like and enjoy. Decluttering can:

- Reduce stress
- Create feelings of calm
- Improve your mental health

Tips for decluttering your home

- **Choose a single room to begin with**. It can be tempting to jump around from room to room, but that can make the process scattered and disorganised. Either pick the room where you spend most of your time, or the one that needs the most attention. Set a timeline – for example, dedicate an hour a day for a week solely to the task.
- **Create a plan of attack**. Before you start, decide what you want to accomplish in the room. For example, if the goal is to update your child's bedroom from the princess theme to something more age appropriate for a pre-teen, make a list of what you need to do and break the overall task down into smaller tasks. Will there be a desk and where will it go? Where can you donate the old dolls and toys? This will help you stay focused and motivated throughout the process.

- **Gather your supplies**. Gather essential decluttering supplies such as bin bags, boxes, containers and cleaning products. Having everything you need on hand will make the process more efficient.
- **Start decluttering**. It's time to get to work! Create five piles in the room: 1) Keep; 2) Donate; 3) Throw away; 4) Recycle; 5) Sell. As you go through the room, decide which pile each item belongs in. Be ruthless and honest with yourself about what you really need and use; don't be afraid to let go of things that no longer serve a purpose in your life. If you have multiple items that serve the same purpose, consider paring down duplicates and keep only what you really need. If you haven't used an item in over a year, it's probably safe to get rid of it. This includes kitchen gadgets, toiletries and that pair of jeans that you wore once 15 years ago after you had lost a few pounds following a stomach bug.
- **Follow through**. Once you've sorted your items into piles, make sure to follow through with getting rid of the unwanted items. Don't be a "half a job, Bob" – keeping the piles sitting in a room is not decluttering! Use those dedicated daily hours to go to the dump, the charity shop, and to sell your unwanted items online.

5

Body Image

We thought long and hard about what to call this chapter and we settled on "body image" rather than "body positivity", as when we practised body positivity for our podcast we both came away with a sense that the body positive movement has some holes.

The idea behind the body positive movement is to love your body regardless of size, shape, skin tone, gender and physical abilities. While we believe this is the ultimate Nirvana for each and every one of us, we are overtly aware this isn't always a possible reach. Nicole will fully admit that, while she lives in her socially acceptably sized, active, healthy body, she has never been able to attain this acceptance, and she is far from alone.

Ask yourself, or any woman for that matter, if she loves every aspect of her body every single day and you'll find very few who are able to say yes.

Women are fundamentally taught to hate their bodies, so feelings of positivity towards our body, for most of us, is impossible.

THE SOCIETY WE LIVE IN

We are constantly told that our self-worth is based on how good we look, or that having cellulite, rolls, extra chins, acne and even body hair in some places is wrong and needs fixing. This skewed reality translates into us spending a lot of time and money on fixing the "problem" of our imperfect bodies. This toxic messaging leaves most women feeling pretty crap about their own body image. If you constantly tune into and focus on your thighs being too big or your boobs not being where they should be, then your overall relationship with yourself will struggle to flourish.

Our relationship with our bodies is complex and, despite slow progress towards embracing all body types in some areas of society, we can still be filled with shame and discontentment.

The global beauty industry alone is worth £471 billion in 2024 and is growing at 8% a year; cosmetics alone are worth £86.5 billion. This is far too much money for these industries to want women to start liking what they see in the mirror. All the marketing in the beauty, fitness, food, diet, skin care and supplement industries are built on targeting women's insecurity and trying to fix an aesthetic "problem" that was created by these industries to begin with. In the words of anti-pornography activist Dr Gail Dines: "If tomorrow women woke up and decided they really liked their bodies, just think how many industries would go out of business."

We hope this chapter will help you with your body image.

WHAT DOES GOOD BODY IMAGE LOOK LIKE?

Having a good body image simply means being comfortable in your own body; that sounds achievable, right? Sadly not. If it was that simple, we'd all be in that place and very few of us are.

BENEFITS OF CREATING A "GOOD BODY IMAGE"

Taking the time to work on your body image can lead to you:

- Feeling confident about your body and yourself
- Being happier

- Accepting your body as it is
- Enjoying the body you have
- Celebrating any of your body's changes that occur naturally due to ageing, pregnancy or lifestyle choices
- Enjoying exercise and movement more
- Enjoying life events
- Wearing anything you want with confidence

This chapter is not about pushing you into an unrealistic place of having to love your body every single day. Rather, it is about building a tangible relationship with your body so that you can trust it, appreciate it and enjoy it for all that it does for you.

Trigger Warning

The practices in this chapter contain detailed discussion of disordered eating. If you have been or are affected by any of the issues raised, then please see the back of the book for places you can reach out to for support and help.

THE PRACTICES

We hope our chosen practices move you towards acceptance and comfort in your own skin and encourage you to be with your body in a positive and connected way.

- **Spending more time naked**
- **Focusing on body neutrality**

SPENDING MORE TIME NAKED

Do you remember romping around the garden, playing in a paddling pool or building a sandcastle on a beach in your birthday suit as a small child? That feeling of freedom, the warm sun and cool air on your bare skin and the unselfconscious happiness that we all have as children vanishes forever once we learn to be ashamed of our nakedness.

According to a survey in *Women's Health*, which polled over 3,500 women:

- 50% spent less than 10 minutes a day in the nude
- 8% felt comfortable with their naked body
- 72% believed they look better fully clothed
- 82% said their cellulite was a potential barrier to baring all
- 21% never have sex with the lights on
- And yet; 53% of women in heterosexual relationships said that their male partners have asked them to get naked more often!

Teaching yourself to be at ease in the nude once again as an adult comes with practice. Many of us are conscious of our flaws. When we are bemoaning the perfectly normal curve of our stomach, we forget that every image we are fed is airbrushed and photoshopped to perfection and that, underneath their clothes, *everybody* – even that supermodel you follow just to make yourself feel bad – has imperfections. Stripping off and baring all is worth it, as it will do wonders for your body image and your self-esteem.

BENEFITS OF GETTING NAKED

- **You become more comfortable with your body**. Many women struggle with their body image, especially after having children.

Matrescence changes things: stretch marks and changes to your breasts, stomach and vulva can be confronting. We have had five children between us, so we get it. Many women have a plethora of ways to avoid having to look at their whole body. When you force yourself to look at your body regularly, you are better able to accept it as it is now. It has carried you through your life and maybe carried your babies too.

- **It raises self-esteem and confidence**. When you are comfortable with the masterpiece that is your beautiful body, you will exude an aura of confidence. Confidence is very attractive, and if you feel comfortable naked, just imagine what a snack you will feel in your clothes!

- **It boosts relationships and encourages intimacy**. If you have a partner, then spending more time naked with them lets them know you trust them and that you're okay with being vulnerable around them. It can naturally lead to more understanding, increased communication and oxytocin-boosting skin-to-skin contact; and yes, more sex too.

- **You get a better night's sleep**. A big factor to better quality sleep is lowering your body temperature. The body is also then in an optimum state to perform the many tasks it needs to do at night, such as renewing cells and eliminating toxins. A lower body temperature will also help you fall asleep quicker, as it slows your metabolism which helps you to relax.

- **It helps with stress and anxiety**. Being naked more often causes a fall in the hormone cortisol, which is what your body releases under stressful conditions. Being naked tells your body it's time to relax.

- **It makes you happier**. Researchers discovered via an online survey that naturists often have higher self-esteem, better body image and were generally happier than their fully clothed peers.

Lauren: Also, it's good for your vagina. Leaving your lady garden to air from time to time can be very healthy. It allows the skin to breathe and helps even out its natural PH balance. If you are not up for going commando, then just try sleeping naked.
Nicole: Vaginas again? Really?
Lauren: Yep.

SELF-CARE STEPS FOR SPENDING MORE TIME NAKED

Take some time every day to just allow your body to be free of clothing. Try any or all of these steps to discover which work best for you.

Step 1: Drink your morning coffee naked

If it's appropriate in your home (e.g., you're not house-sharing or the parent of teenagers who will be absolutely mortified by the sight of your bits and pieces out on display), start the day with coffee in the nude – please be careful not to spill it!

Step 2: Get dressed last

After your shower or bath, do your hair and make-up naked before getting dressed. This will force you to stare at yourself in all your glory.

Step 3: Be a naturist

If you have access to a private outdoor space or balcony where you are not overlooked, then sit outside naked with a book or a drink and soak up some vitamin D. Don't forget sun protection – burnt boobies are not a good look!

Step 4: Strip off when no one is home

Take advantage of being the only one home by shedding your clothes and hanging out as naked as the day you were born. Just remember you're naked before opening the front door to an unsuspecting delivery driver and make sure you know when everyone is expected home if those people would not be delighted to be greeted by a nude you (if they would be, then, hey, go for it!).

Step 5: Sleep in the nude

Pull off the PJs and say no to the nightie – and it's a no-sie to the onesie – just slide under your duvet happy in the skin you are in and enjoy all the related benefits.

OUR EXPERIENCE

Lauren

My husband has been looking at my naked body for the last 27 years – what a lucky guy! When he first saw it, it was pretty cute. It was a smaller, tighter, perter body that had not yet housed, grown, birthed and breastfed our three beautiful sons. The thing is, even back when we met, my body was not "perfect". In the decades that followed, he has seen me naked in all stages of pregnancy, giving birth (that's like the extreme sports version of being naked) and my postpartum body, complete with a newly evacuated blancmange belly, cracked, bleeding nipples and engorged breasts. I wanted to ask him how he felt about my naked body now that gravity and three children have morphed it into something different, but I realised that it was entirely irrelevant, as the only person whose opinion is important and valid on this subject is my own.

Of course, let's not forget that men's bodies age too. My husband's body is also 27 years older than the one I first saw. It does not change my love for him or my attraction to him. It would never occur to me to not accept him and the body he lives in, just as he accepts mine.

This practice was not a stretch for me, as I discovered that I seem to be naked more often than I realise. We both sleep naked; although I have been known to wear socks on a snowy night as it's not appreciated when I attempt to tuck my freezing feet up into my husband's warm, sleeping body. I am happy to walk around my bedroom naked, and I never lock the door when I'm in the shower or bath – the boys have learnt the hard way not to barge in and ask for a lift to the station. I don't feel a need to hide myself.

I usually get dressed last. This isn't an intentional thing, it's just a habit, but it means that after a morning shower I have a good 20 minutes standing naked in front of the mirror while I put on make-up and dry my hair. I think this regular exposure brings an acceptance of my naked form. Or maybe I'm just a naturist at heart?

Nicole: *You would make a great naturist.*
Lauren: *I'll take that as a compliment.*

Having spent 16 years as a birth doula I have seen naked bodies of all shapes and sizes. I am very accepting of the naked form and it's not something that holds any shock factor for me. I spent the latter part of my teenage years wearing as little clothing as was humanly possible without being arrested for indecent exposure. I thought nothing of showing off my body. Nowadays, I am a bit curvier, a stone and a half heavier with breasts that need scaffolding, a more rounded stomach, and legs that are not the slim limbs I once owned. I don't spend much time, if any at all, thinking about these changes, although I am often surprised when I see old photos.

Nicole

Before I jump into my experience, I would like give you a bit of background to something deeply personal, which is perhaps the inspiration behind this chapter. I have a historically complicated relationship with my body.

When I was a teenager, I was blessed with huge boobs, a small waist and a flat tummy. I also had what my community likes to call "Jewish thighs", which is code for chunky. I remember walking down the street one day and a stranger (a man) said to me, "Wow! Those are some child-bearing hips." I laughed it off at the time, but it's something I still occasionally think about. Another time, a hairdressing client (a woman) asked if she could be honest with me. Before I could reply she slapped me on the arse and said, "Such a pretty face, but such a big bottom."

I often wonder if those moments were the starting points to my toxic relationship with my body. Other than these few unpleasant comments, I always felt pretty good about myself, and this lasted through to my 20s. I have always had what is now termed as "thin privilege".

I hit my 30s, had my two daughters, and then my obsession with being thin and lean began. I had two very young children, and I was finding parenting challenging. My husband, Adam, was travelling for work most of the time and not home as much as I probably needed him to be. I had a dynamic hairdressing career in TV and editorial work, but with both Adam and myself travelling for work, it was becoming unmanageable. I stepped back from a job I loved and set up a private hair salon from home. What was intended to give me a happy balance between motherhood and my career left me uninspired and with a sense of guilt for not feeling satisfied. I was lonely, I needed an escape and the gym gave me just that. It's a difficult admission, but it is my truth nonetheless.

I instantly became hooked. I started exercising every day, changed my diet and toned up to the point of having a six-pack. Everywhere I went, I was complimented on my transformation and I became heavily reliant on the attention. What they didn't notice were the skipped meals, the times I would rush out of the house to get to the gym as soon as my husband got home and miss the girls' bath and bedtime, and how exercise and dieting became my sole focus until it was untenable – it affected my marriage, some friendships and my self-esteem.

At my lowest point I was in size six jeans (that was quite a moment for my "Jewish thighs"). I had anxiety whenever I had to eat out of the house, and I surrounded myself with people who indulged me and my lifestyle. Simple, everyday things, like putting the weekly shopping away, became almost impossible and I would sleep every afternoon when the girls napped because I was always exhausted; my periods became sporadic and I felt the need to escape the family unit as often as I could. I wasn't functioning.

It was awful, especially for my loved ones. They tried to talk to me, but I convinced myself they didn't understand and it was part of their failing, not mine. I also told myself that I was being "healthy", which it was anything but. I still hold shame around this period of my life.

This episode lasted four years and took another three for me to find any kind of healthy balance. It took therapy, patience, support and a desire to get better. Learning to let go of the body I worked so hard to create but which only brought misery, took a long time; but, today, I am proud to say I am back to a healthy and happy size.

However, I was not delighted with the challenge to be naked more.

I chose to do this practice when we were on a short break away, so having my morning coffee naked wasn't an option unless I wanted to get arrested for indecent exposure (which by the way I didn't).

When I mentioned to my 15-year-old what we were practising this week she looked horrified and said, "Mum are you going to go down to the lobby naked?" I assured her I wasn't but it said a lot about what levels she thinks we stoop to on the podcast!

The first day, I did my make-up in front of the mirror naked – I hated it, I was cold.

We came home a few days later from the mini break. Feeling bloated and a few pounds heavier, I thought it was a good time to try this practice again. After my shower I remained naked. Again, it was cold and exposing. I got dressed and went to bed upset with myself at how hard I was finding this practice.

The next day I wanted to give the naked coffee a whirl – now there's a sentence I never thought I'd say. Here's what was different this time: I caught myself in the mirror and, instead of baulking, with a kind inner voice I found myself saying, "Look at your amazing healthy body; look at how it houses you and carries you. You are lucky." That was quite the mental shift.

WHAT DID WE LEARN?
Lauren
I am accepting of the ageing process and the natural changes to the shell I walk around in. Do I love it? No. If I could wave a wand and magic it back to how it looked at age 18, would I? Yes! But the sad fact is that, back then, I never appreciated how I looked – I just took it for granted. But I am learning to accept my naked body just as it is.

Nicole

Being naked should be the most natural thing in the world, but it's a real edge for me – it kicks off a nasty dialogue about my body's imperfections, but once I quieten that down it feels pretty freeing. I loved making my morning coffee in the nude; it felt naughty and intimate. This has been a micro-metamorphosis for me.

BODY NEUTRALITY

Body neutrality focuses on what your body can do for you rather than what it actually looks like. It differs from body positivity because it's not about loving your body but being accepting of it. Instead of being absorbed with your physical appearance, the focus is on your body's *abilities*. It teaches us to steer our focus away from society's expectations of how it "should" look and focus on what our body is doing, so we can learn to appreciate our bodies in a much healthier, more realistic way.

The human body is an incredible piece of machinery which is housing us and working for us every minute of every day, and this gets overlooked in favour of a much less important issue of how beach body ready we are.

Fun Fact

If you have a body and you're on the beach, congratulations! You have a beach body.

Your body is pulling air into your lungs, pumping blood round your body, seeing the world around you, hearing every sound (unless you are one of our children and we've just asked you to clear the table), tasting the food you eat and feeling a huge range of emotions (especially when it's that time of the month). These are just a few of the wondrous things your body is simultaneously doing without you even having to think about it.

Being able-bodied is a privilege that not everyone has the luxury of experiencing, and we both feel very grateful to have been afforded this throughout our lives. You may be living with different challenges from your body, but we hope this chapter highlights a common issue for everyone, regardless of size, gender and ability and whatever challenges you may face.

The body neutrality movement encourages us to step back from conversations about our appearance, and allow ourselves to enjoy our bodies and even accept them.

In a world built on self-hate, it is a radical act to love ourselves.

SELF-CARE STEPS TO BODY NEUTRALITY

Step 1: Think of what your body is doing for you

Your body supports you unconditionally – even when you speak hate to it, it will still show up for you as best it can. If you have just eaten a big meal and your first reaction is to jump to guilt, stop and ask: "How is my body digesting this food? Did that meal give me energy for the rest of the day/ evening? How did the food taste?"

Step 2: Ask yourself: "How is my body loving me right now?"

Remember: your body is always working in ways to support you. When you have those nasty thoughts about your thighs being too big or your stomach too rounded, find that focus and ask yourself this beautiful question: "How is my body loving me right now?"

Step 3: Daily affirmation

Every time you catch yourself being cruel about your body, remind yourself, "I am allowed to enjoy the body I live in and it is imperative to my wellbeing." Living in self-hatred is so normalised that we barely notice we are even in that mindset. You may not like how your body looks, but you are allowed to enjoy your body despite what you have been conditioned to think.

Step 4: Reframe why exercise is important to you

Instead of fixating on burning calories or building your abs, feel how your body is moving, how the exercise can lift your mood and is strengthening your body. Think of all the non-aesthetic ways exercise adds to your life.

Step 5: Gratitude

Every day, think of one thing you are grateful to your body for and thank it. Gratitude is the gift that keeps on giving. Do steps 2 and 5 together – it's a game-changing combination.

Step 6: Only keep clothes that fit now and make you feel good

This will help you to feel more confident, and will reduce anxiety and self-flagellation when you get dressed every morning.

Step 7: Get rid of the scales

Scales bring discontent – a machine does not need to define your worth and mood.

OUR EXPERIENCE

Lauren

I have always had a healthy relationship with my body and with food. I have never dieted, and my body size, shape and weight are not something I have ever really spent a lot of time thinking about.

I love cooking, eating and feeding others. Food to me is life, it is family, it is love. I have unfortunately seen at close quarters what illness can do to the body. Bearing witness to seeing people you love wasting away as cancer ravages their body has made me no longer associate "very thin" with anything "good". I think it's smart to have a few spare pounds as insurance. Genetics gave me the body size I was born with, and my family are all naturally slim. This is not to say that I am particularly fit or strong. I live in a body that is considered "socially acceptable", and I have no lived experience of existing any other way. I am also privileged to be able-bodied, and feel exceptionally lucky for the robust health I have enjoyed all of my life and for everything that my body has done for me. It has served me, and even overcome fertility issues in order to allow me to carry and birth my children. These are not things that I take for granted. I have also found that with age comes more acceptance of my body shape as it changes. I don't watch Love Island wishing I could pull off a thong bikini with underboob.

For this practice, I put on a dress made of a thin jersey material that clung in all the wrong places. I knew that every time I went to wear it, I was going to feel self-conscious. Why would I choose to walk around all day in something that made me feel bad about a body that, on the whole, I am okay with? So, I gave it to the charity shop – it felt liberating.

Later in the practice week, I had to go swimwear shopping, which is certainly not my favourite activity. Every summer since I turned 40, my arse is a bit lower, my tummy a bit bigger, my waist a bit thicker. In the changing room I got to see each and every flaw in the 360° mirrors and the most unflattering lighting. A few pieces fitted in my normal size ... others certainly did not. Seeing myself in all my glory, attempting to squeeze into the size I wanted to be in was in equal parts comic and tragic. Once it was finally on, it dug into my flesh and pinched me; I looked awful and was uncomfortable. I gave myself a good stern talking to in the mirror. I told myself I was being stubborn and ridiculous – that my pride and vanity were getting in the way of actually looking better in something that fitted me and supported me. They were not going to put out an in-store tannoy at the checkout saying, "Attention everyone. Please look at the woman at till number four. She's gone up a size." In fact, not a single living being ever had to even know what size I was buying. I reminded myself that my value is not determined by an arbitrary number on a label. So, I marched back to the display and took the size up. And, because it fitted, it looked better and I could breathe. And you know what happened? ... NOTHING! The world didn't stop turning. A parade of people with placards did not storm into the changing room to mock me and it didn't go viral. Because NOBODY CARES. I wore that swimsuit on my healthy and perfectly functioning body that I am very grateful for while sitting by a pool with my kids and husband who all give zero fucks what I wear, and a bunch of strangers I'll never see again and who I strongly suspect did not have their entire holiday ruined because the woman on the sunbed next to theirs went up one size.

Nicole

I can't really tell you how my practice went with body neutrality as it has become so ingrained into my psyche and something I now practise every day. What I can tell you is that the self-care steps in this practice saved me from myself and brought me back to life.

My lightbulb moment came a few years back when I came across a photo from two years earlier. I remembered the photo being taken when I was having a check-in at a bodybuilding gym I was a member of. These check-ins involved standing in a bikini, having photos taken of you from all angles, then discussing what parts of your body needed attention and what your diet would (and wouldn't) consist of for the next week. It only ever included weighed-out chicken, sweet potatoes, oats, tuna and the occasional banana thrown in – but only after training. The day the photo was taken, I remember feeling overweight and dreading the thought of a semi-naked photo being taken in front of numerous people deciding what was "wrong" with me. Please know, not only did I fully subscribe to this, I was paying for the service.

I looked at this photo during the practice week and saw skin and bone. There was not an ounce of fat on me, and my once-curvaceous figure had turned childlike. No child-bearing hips to see here peeps, just muscle and a very unhappy woman. This was the moment I knew I had to climb out of the black hole I had willingly jumped into.

I slowly stepped away from the sweet potatoes, the occasional banana, the community I was hiding in and the gym I went to – and I eventually found myself again. I reintegrated with my loved ones and started to eat a more balanced diet. I remember eating a piece of melon after not having eaten it for years, and wanting to cry. Every small step – of which there were thousands – brought me back to myself.

Now I am a member of a gym that only pushes and assesses my performance, which works swimmingly with the body neutrality ideology. My current gym crew exercise because they want to be fit, fast and strong. These are my people. I am still careful with what I eat because I like to be healthy, but not to the point of control because I want to enjoy my life to the fullest (and a life without Oreos is no life at all). Body neutrality taught me how to do that.

Once I gained weight, I gained my life back. I still like to maintain the weight and dress size I am; call that conditioning or call it a choice, I'm not sure which it is, but I know where I feel comfortable with my body.

WHAT DID WE LEARN?
Lauren
Ever been to a party and had a shit time because the hostess has put on 5lbs?

I didn't think so.

I concluded at the end of the week that it's all in your attitude. If you are happy, loving, confident and accepting of yourself, that's the message you will put out into the world. I don't spend a lot of time thinking about how my body looks, but I do consider what it has given me: my children and continuous health. My body works for me every day on autopilot; it is a beautifully functioning machine.

Nicole
Body neutrality saved me from my old obsessions around aesthetic perfection. By changing the conversation with myself about how my body is rather than how my body isn't and what my body does rather than what it doesn't do, allowed me to step into a much more loving narrative. Every day, my body does exactly what I tell it to do. If I want to go for a six-mile walk, I do; if I want to run around my local park and do lunges, I do.

My body is strong, loyal, supportive and, best of all, healthy. I love what my body does for me and it loves me back; even when I speak hate to it, it continues to show up for me. This is a huge privilege and defining myself only within the confines of how my body looks is quite frankly disrespectful to this privilege. This practice has taken me from self-loathing to self-acceptance and has changed my entire life.

TAKE-AWAY TIPS

Spending more time naked
The more time you spend naked the more normal the sight of your naked body will be: as the shock factor reduces, acceptance increases.

Body neutrality
Exercise because you *love* your body, not because you hate it. Think of all the ways your body is loving you.

If you struggle with your body image, please go through the steps again and again and again. They *will* change the way you relate to your body, and the results are empowering and freeing.

READER CHALLENGES

Lauren's challenge
Whenever you go to criticise your body, instead say three nice things about it out loud. How your body looks is the least interesting thing about you.

Nicole's challenge
Being able to cultivate a healthy relationship with exercise has been fundamental to every area of my life. Exercise brings out the very best in me, and without it I wouldn't be half as driven, active, healthy or disciplined – and I want that for you.

Side note: I want it for Lauren too but she refuses to play.

If you are stuck in the cycle of exercising for aesthetic gains, you will miss all the beauty that exercise offers. This challenge allows your perspective to be widened.

Before you exercise, think of three non-aesthetic reasons why you are doing it. And if you can't think of three, then you can't go – yep, I am being that strict. Exercise is a beautiful way to honour your body, not a reason to hate on it. To give you some inspiration, the reasons I now train are:

- To keep my body strong and healthy
- To stay fit to aid my lifestyle
- To clear my head
- To help with my migraines
- For my mental health
- To move my body
- To help my bad back
- To get the blood moving round my body
- To help with anxiety
- To help with overwhelm
- To de-stress
- To be a part of a community
- To have fun
- To feel alive
- To achieve something
- To hit a PB (personal best)
- To feel proud of myself

6

Physical Health

Let's take a look at our physical health. If you have come here looking for guidance on how to perfect your abs or your Vinyasa flow, then prepare to be a disappointed downward dog. Perfection (and yoga) are not what this book is about.

There will be no hard rules about having to do five HIIT classes a week while living on charcoal-activated water and acai bowls (but if that's your thing, then good for you!). This chapter is purely about finding the joy that lives in your body and looking after it in a way that makes you feel good. Your body is the only house you will ever live in, so we want you to cultivate a relationship with it that is kind and empowering.

With the global health and fitness industry worth an estimated £100 billion in 2024, and an endless well of fitness disciplines on offer, it is no wonder that you might not know where to begin. Every week, it seems, a new fitness trend emerges – from aerial yoga to CrossFit, we are constantly fed contradictions on what will improve our health and our lives. With so much information at our fingertips, how can we know what we can trust and what is the best approach?

Our answer to this is: do whatever works for you.

Self-care is about your own personal journey of bringing wellbeing and joy to your life – and your physical health is at the top of that list. This chapter is about allowing you the space to reflect on where you are at physically and where you want to get to.

Many health professionals offer a simple framework for taking control of our health. They are condensed into five basic pillars: Nutrition, Exercise, Hydration, Relaxation and Sleep. The premise is that if these five things are in place, then essentially you will be "well". We are going to tackle exercise and sleep in our practices, but let's take a look at the other pillars first.

NUTRITION

When we talk about physical health, the food we consume plays a vital role in our overall wellbeing. As neither of us are trained nutritionists or dieticians, we felt such an epic topic is best left to the professionals. Creating a balance with your nutrition can be easier said than done and the conversation around the best way to eat is relentless. With new diets continuing to flood the wellness world, it can be impossible to know where to start. Intermittent fasting, keto, plant based, paleo, dairy free, gluten free, low carb, high carb, high fibre, high fat, low fat, Atkins, calorie counting, macro counting – these are just a few of the trends over the years that claimed to give us the elixir of life. There is an abundance of content around nutrition with thousands of podcasts, books, TV programmes and social channels dedicated to how to eat well. We invite you to explore this for yourself and find a way to nourish your body that suits your lifestyle. At the back of the book are suggestions of places that offer help around nutrition.

HYDRATION

We argue constantly about the benefits of staying hydrated. Nicole has a water bottle to hand at all times, sipping, gulping, slurping; especially when recording the show which drives Lauren insane. As a result of this incessant sipping, she also needs to wee as often a toddler on a plane. Lauren drinks only coffee or wine and prefers to dehydrate or as she likes to call it "remain dry" (a bit like her humour). Lauren argues Nicole cannot possibly need all this water as she spends most of the day relieving herself of it; Nicole insists hydration is key in order to flush any toxins out of your body. Lauren does not buy into the toxins debate and thinks it's fine to drink only when you are thirsty and not for the sake of it.

Make of that what you will.

Nicole: *But just make sure you stay hydrated!*

RELAXATION

There is a plethora of ways to relax, to aid you in taking a pause from the hectic pace of life. Lauren relaxes through cooking and reading while Nicole finds walking and going to the gym the best way to unwind: two very different approaches, but equally effective. Relaxation is personal, so we all need to find whatever works to take us away from everyday stress and noise and help us to be present.

A few examples include:

- Meeting up with a friend
- Going to a film, an exhibition, live music or a show
- Crafting
- Knitting
- Yoga, Pilates or gentle stretching
- Meditation
- Jigsaws
- Drawing or painting
- Playing with your pet
- Napping

Fun Fact

Lauren and Nicole both find watching Real Housewives *hugely relaxing, but we figured this probably shouldn't go in a self-care book as a legit tip!*

Yet here we are.

THE PRACTICES

We are very different from one another in how we look after our physical health. Nicole is terrible at sitting still, whereas Lauren loves it. Lauren hates exercise, and Nicole can't get enough of it. However, we are both "well" and both take time for ourselves. There is no right or wrong and no fixed rules here. All we ask is that you take the time for yourself to keep physically well, and do it in a way that makes you happy.

The practices we have chosen for this chapter are:

- **Sleep hygiene**
- **Awe walking**
- **Couch to 5K**

SLEEP HYGIENE

Sleep is considered the most important of the pillars of health, but many of us have evenings when we find it hard to fall asleep, sleep fitfully or wake in the night. Sleep problems often resolve themselves in a short period of time, but when longer stretches of sleep issues or insomnia become ongoing they can start to affect our lives. There is an enormous body of guidance and advice that's been gathered in the last decade – from it, we chose a practice that we found fundamental: sleep hygiene.

THE DOWNSIDES OF NOT GETTING ENOUGH SLEEP

- The mind and body can't properly recharge.
- Your thinking, memory and decision-making are affected.
- You suffer with daytime sleepiness, which can harm productivity and achievement.
- You may be irritable and struggle to regulate your emotions.
- Sleep deprivation is connected to mental health disorders, such as depression and anxiety.
- It worsens your physical health – increasing risk of dementia and diabetes.
- It reduces your sex hormone production.
- It's bad for your weight. (Bet we have your attention now, don't we?)

Most adults need between seven and nine hours a night, but apparently 1–3% of the population – the "sleepless elite" – live happily on just a few hours a night. One of this number was Arianna Huffington, best known as the co-founder and former editor-in-chief of *The Huffington Post*. But these days, she is a sleep evangelist. Before her sleep epiphany, she was surviving on three or four hours' sleep a night, she found decision-making difficult and said she was "more irritable, more reactive, less present and absolutely less joyful in my life". In 2007, she collapsed in her office and broke her cheekbone. Her doctors told her she was exhausted. The experience led Huffington to completely change her own habits and advocate for others to do the same. She became a sleep expert and wrote a bestselling book, *The Sleep Revolution* (WH Allen, 2017).

Huffington follows a strict evening routine, which she describes as a "sacrosanct ritual". She starts off by "escorting" her electronic devices out of her room, followed by a hot bath with Epsom salts. She then changes into "clothes that are specifically designated for sleep". (We call these "pyjamas", but each to their own.) She drinks herbal tea, writes down the things that she is grateful for that day, and reads actual books in bed that have nothing to do with work. She doesn't set an alarm, and wakes naturally after about eight hours of sleep.

Huffington says that longer and better sleep has meant she is, without question, a better leader, and that it is sheer delusion that in order to succeed as an entrepreneur you need to burn out. She also says sleep is evolutionary, and if we ignore that need, we will pay a huge price in every aspect of our health and cognitive performance.

BENEFITS OF SLEEP HYGIENE

A healthy bedtime routine:

- Improves decision making
- Improves long-term physical and mental health
- Reduces stress and improves your mood
- Makes you feel happier
- Improves weight management
- Restores energy and health
- Helps the brain flush out harmful toxins
- Regulates metabolism and hormones
- Helps muscles and organs to repair and recover

SELF-CARE STEPS FOR SLEEP HYGIENE

Step 1: Implement pro-sleep habits during the day

A good night's sleep starts with what you do during the day; preparing for high-quality sleep is an all-day affair. Here are a handful of steps that you can take during the day to pave the way for better sleep at night.

- Spend time outside in daylight.
- Exercise (but not too close to bedtime).
- Don't consume caffeine after 2pm.
- Avoid alcohol last thing at night.
- Don't eat dinner too late.
- Reserve your bedroom for sleep and sex only – don't hang out or work there.

Step 2: Optimise your sleep schedule
- Have a fixed waking time every day including weekends.
- Aim for between seven and nine hours of sleep a night.

Step 3: Create a sleep-inducing bedroom
- Make sure your mattress, pillows, bed linen and covers are comfortable.
- Keep it dark (black out curtains, eye mask).
- Make sure it's peaceful and quiet (use earplugs if needed).
- Make sure the room is the right temperature as being too hot or too cold will disturb you (optimum temperature is 18°C).
- Have a nice aroma in the room, like lavender.

Unfun Fact
Lauren sleeps with an elderly 25kg Spaniel on the bed, so often the night-time aroma is dog farts.

Step 4: Create a pre-bedtime routine
- Wind down for at least 30 minutes (try quiet reading, low-impact stretching, listening to soothing music).
- Have a warm bath or shower.
- Put on comfortable nightwear.

- Lower the lights; avoid bright light and blue light.
- Disconnect from devices for at least 30 minutes before bed; preferably remove them from the room completely.

OUR EXPERIENCE

Lauren

I sleep like the dead. I have slept on plastic chairs in labour wards, the floor of my children's bedrooms, on trains, planes, a boat that was being thrown around in a storm, buses, cars and, according to my parents, bolt upright on a luggage trolley at Heathrow airport. I don't need darkness, music or any accessories, and I don't wake in the night. I'm very grateful for this ability. In fact, rather than experiencing sleeplessness in times of stress, the opposite applies: I am a person who will sleep their way out of trauma: the worse things are, the more I will sleep. My body just shuts down.

However, I have a lifetime habit of staying up late. I have always been a night owl, and I remember even at 13 I was sneaking downstairs to watch Prisoner Cell Block H (for anyone under 40 that was the 1980s equivalent of Orange is the New Black) at 1.30am. My average bedtime is around midnight because I absolutely love a late-night TV binge and the quiet time alone on the sofa with nobody needing me or asking anything of me.

My practice week was mixed.

The first three nights we practised sleep hygiene I had a stomach bug that came out of nowhere. I felt so grim that early nights were enforced upon me as I was totally wiped out. By 9pm each night I was tucked up and fast asleep. There is no TV in my room, so I read a little before sleeping and left my phone downstairs to charge. By the fourth night I felt better, so my bad habits returned. At 10.15pm, after the TV show we were watching ended, I decided it was far too early to go to bed and set myself an "early night" rule of 11pm. I only managed two nights of this before binge-watching Netflix until 2.35am on a school night. It is my way of carving out time for myself, and it's a bit rebellious. Please don't think I'm not aware of how tragic it is that this is how I rebel. Rock'n'roll it ain't.

Nicole

Sleep is very important to me, and my worst feeling is that of being tired. I like to feel rested and if I sleep any less than six hours, I really feel it. It makes me very, very grumpy. There is a TV in our bedroom, and we always watch something before we go to sleep, which I now realise is totally against sleep hygiene rules. According to sleep experts, journaling and reading is meant to be better for you, but clearly, they've never seen an episode of Vanderpump Rules.

As I've gotten older, I wake up much earlier. This is thanks to my bladder, which seems to need to be emptied every three minutes throughout the night. That's been a lovely new development: I'm basically turning into my mother.

Lauren: No, it's because you drink 20 litres of water a day.
Nicole: I'm not having the hydration debate again.

A lie in for me is 8am, and I'm good with that. There is nothing better than an early night and waking up bright and early to workout.

Needless to say, my habits around sleep aren't the best, mainly because it's not an area of struggle for me.

The practice week started out with a row with my husband as he likes to fall asleep with the TV on, and when I informed him that that shit needed to stop ASAP on "sleep hygiene week" he was less than pleased. I won the argument, and instead of falling asleep with the telly on we had a conversation, which was pretty novel after 15 years of marriage – and he slept peacefully all night. He refused to admit those two facts were linked.

Night two, and I bossed it again: I turned my phone off, read my book and it felt very nourishing. I even contemplated journaling, but I fell asleep before I could find a pen.

Night four, I cheated (following rules for too long is always a personal challenge): we discovered Stranger Things on Netflix, so sleep hygiene went straight out the window as we binged the hell out of it.

I basically failed. Miserably.

WHAT DID WE LEARN?
Lauren

There are very few things that are fun about being an adult, but one is that you can go to bed whenever the hell you want – and I still wish to exercise my right to do this.

I also learnt during the research for the show that I indulge in a known phenomenon called "revenge bedtime procrastination". This is the decision to delay or sacrifice sleep for leisure time and a few hours of entertainment in response to stress or lack of free time earlier in the day, even though it results in insufficient sleep. The phrase emerged from a Chinese expression that reflected frustration tied to long, stressful work hours that left little time for personal enjoyment. Three factors make up bedtime procrastination.

- *A delay in going to sleep that reduces your total sleep time.*
- *The absence of a valid reason for staying up later than intended, such as an external event or an underlying illness (Married at First Sight Australia is not a valid reason).*
- *An awareness that delaying your bedtime could lead to negative consequences.*

I have all three!

Nicole

I am a naturally good sleeper and I realised I do a lot of the steps naturally. I don't drink coffee after 2pm (okay, 4pm); I don't drink a lot of alcohol as I know it interrupts my sleep; I have black-out curtains and an eye mask; I go to bed at a reasonable time; I wake up early and I mostly exercise in the mornings. #winning

I could be better with my phone and the TV, but at this point I don't feel it is impacting my sleep, so Vanderpump Rules stays.

AWE WALKING

Arguably overused in the 1990s, when "awesome" became synonymous with describing anything that was "vaguely okay", the concept of awe is, perhaps, misunderstood.

By cultivating a mindset of noticing awe in the everyday, we become more grounded in the present moment. The latest clinical research also suggests that an awe-filled attitude might be socially beneficial to society as a whole.

The simple act of walking in nature on a short "awe" walk for just 15 minutes, where you make a conscious effort to look for things to be amazed by, can combat negative emotions. It can also help to cultivate mindfulness and have a dramatic effect on your mood.

BENEFITS OF AWE WALKING

A regular awe walk:

- Boosts immunity
- Improves memory and attention span by 20%

- Reduces risk of diabetes and heart disease in middle age by improving cardiovascular health
- Promotes social connection
- Reduces self-focus
- Increases positive emotions like compassion and gratitude
- Lowers stress
- Relaxes the brain

Fun Fact

According to a study published in 2019 by psychologists from the University of Michigan, the effects of awe walking were so potent that the team suggested medical professionals prescribe "nature pills" to combat stress.

So, how should you go about taking an awe walk? Wherever you are, the key is to be in the right frame of mind and turn your ordinary walk into a series of awe-inspiring moments.

SELF-CARE STEPS FOR AWE WALKING

Step 1: Turn off your phone
Or, even better, leave it at home.

Step 2: Take a deep breath in
Count to six as you inhale and six as you exhale. Feel the air moving through your body.

Step 3: Feel your feet on the ground and listen to the sounds around you

Step 4: Shift your awareness to what you can see around you

Step 5: As you walk, bring attention back to your breath occasionally

As you breathe, really take time to notice the sights, smells and noises around you.

As you go through your day, keep your eyes peeled for opportunities for moments that inspire awe and give you goosebumps. It could be listening to a busker or watching the ducks on a local pond.

OUR EXPERIENCE

Lauren

Walking every day isn't optional for me because we have Barker the Springer Spaniel. Springers are a cross between Bear Grylls and an over-caffeinated Davina McCall: they love mud, water and exploring, and are impossible to tire.

I often multi-task as I walk. Ticking things off my to-do list may have nothing to do with awe, but ordering bits of school uniform and editing the online food shop while taking the dog out does give a sense of achievement.

I live opposite woodland, and I take great joy in how the environment changes with the seasons. It gets bleak and horrendously muddy for a few months. When it snows, everything looks like Narnia, and then life slowly returns. The summer is full of long grass and wildflowers. There is awe to be found in every season.

On my first awe walk of the practice week, I headed for an open glade surrounded by horse chestnut trees. It was coming toward the end of autumn – one of my favourite times of year – when the myriad of changing colours in the landscape and the fun of picking up fallen conkers provides a mindful experience. I never fail to be amazed at how completely engrossed and content my kids were year after year spending hours picking up conkers and putting them in a bag. Collecting conkers is an activity that always makes me feel happy.

I wondered as I walked if it was just me who shouts a cheery "Good morning!" to every passing stranger. I realised that, as a Londoner, it's a habit exclusively reserved for the woods – I would never dream of greeting people on the tube or when walking down Oxford Street.

I know my woods so well, each route and every path. I wondered if it was possible to still find awe down a well-trodden path and if that was a metaphor for life. Was I cheating by not exploring new places?

The next day it got a bit meta. I was splashing about in a tiny stream that had been formed because of the recent heavy rainfall. I was thinking about how these tiny rivulets of water all run into a bigger stream, that runs into a river, that eventually meets an ocean, and how we are just insignificant drops. Yes, I was having an existential moment. Nature was connecting me back to Earth, to something bigger than myself and out of my own head. I had found the awe!

Nicole

I walk everyday as I have a lot of energy to burn off. I'm like a six-year-old in that sense.

It was one of those weeks when life decided to chuck all sorts of grenades my way and I went into the week highly stressed, so the awe walks had a lot of work to do. It typically poured with rain all week – a fact Lauren and I seem to disagree on which was fairly odd as we live three miles away from one another. Maybe she was so ensconced in awe that she didn't notice the rain-pocalypse in North London, but it was definitely there for me and trying to find awe in the pissing rain isn't exactly my activity of choice. Rain makes my hair frizzy, and anything that makes my hair a frizzaster is something I immediately disengage from.

Rain and ruined hair aside, I went for my first awe walk. While I walked, I listened to a moving meditation which helped bring my awareness into my body and got me in touch with some very basic miracles that live around us. I watched the beauty of the bond between a mother and her toddler playing together, and took in a majestic oak tree that I walk past every day without ever noticing. I saw everything with a new, brighter lens. I came home on a high that lasted hours. I felt calm and alive.

I wish I could tell you the rest of the week continued in the same vein, but the rain did not let up (unless you were Lauren) and frizzy hair and walking in the rain ain't what I call self-care. I had experienced the awe and I loved it, but when my hair was being threatened by the vicious tsunami, I waved the white flag.

WHAT DID WE LEARN?
Lauren

Walking always makes me feel better. It is one of the easiest ways to change your mood. Whether alone or laughing and talking with a friend, it is vital to my wellbeing. I have never gone for a walk and felt worse afterwards. The dog keeps me present; he is happy to be out and to be alive, regardless of the weather. Dogs are fantastic for so many reasons, but I think even if you just take from them their ability to be in the moment it is beneficial. I love nature, I don't care that Nicole teases me about knowing all the names of trees. When you are a cynical person like me, it's good to keep awe and wonder in your life. It keeps you open. Awe walking is one of the only practices that I continue to use daily. I suspect that I will continue to walk into old age with a canine companion by my side.

Nicole

Looking and experiencing the awe was magical and really brightened my mood. My high lasted a good few hours, but one walk wasn't going to sustain me for the entire week. Walking with awe every day or a few times a week is what I would recommend – it could be completely life changing.

I also learnt that there is no product in the world that can keep rain from making your hair frizz.

COUCH TO 5K

Couch to 5K is a free nine-week running plan for absolute beginners. It is designed to help people transform a sedentary lifestyle into an active one. The plan aims to get the user working out for 20 to 30 minutes, three days a week, and promises to get you in good enough shape to successfully finish a 5-kilometre (3.1-mile) run by the end of the programme.

The Couch to 5K (aka C25K) running plan was created by Josh Clark in 1996. In his early 20s, Josh was suffering from a bad break-up and found he had a lot of excess energy to burn, so he started running. Josh says, "Exercise wasn't something I ever enjoyed. I always found it hard and boring. I remember, in those early days, putting on my shoes and thinking, *Why am I doing this?* But after a few weeks, all that pain and discomfort faded away and it started to feel really good – meditative, even."

At that point, Josh wanted to figure out a way that people could avoid that pain and discomfort he experienced in those first few weeks and find a way to feel the rewards of running straight away – and Couch to 5K was born.

In the mid 2000s, C25K started to build huge momentum. In 2010, the NHS endorsed it as an official exercise plan, and even has an app and a podcast. Over one million people downloaded the NHS Couch to 5K podcast in 2022 alone. This is a 92% increase compared to 2019. Meanwhile, an incredible 6.46 million runs were completed across the UK between 1 January and 29 December 2022 using the app.

Couch to 5K works because it starts with a mix of running and walking to gradually build up your fitness and stamina. This is called interval training. Your first week will consist of three runs. With a mixture of 60-second light jogs and 90-second walks over 20 to 30 minutes. This creates realistic expectations and makes the challenge feel achievable right from the start. As the weeks go on, the running intervals increase while the walking intervals decrease, improving your stamina and endurance slowly and effectively.

BENEFITS OF COUCH TO 5K
Undertaking a running challenge such as Couch to 5K:

- Is an easy, quick way of improving your physical health
- Will improve the health of your heart and lungs
- Is good for your mental health and releases endorphins
- Can help you lose weight, especially if combined with a healthy diet
- May help increase bone density in some people, which can help protect against bone diseases like osteoporosis
- Can boost your self-esteem, giving you a sense of direction and achievement

SELF-CARE STEPS FOR COUCH TO 5K

Step 1: Download the Couch to 5K app

Step 2: Enjoy it!

OUR EXPERIENCE

Lauren

I must take full responsibility and say that despite all the moaning this was my idea. But I only chose it because Nicole had something so much worse in mind (gym sessions with a personal trainer for a month). Nevertheless, I was dreading it. This was not my first foray into the programme – it was, in fact, my third. Even though the first two were interrupted by injury, the huffing and puffing, the general exertion and the aching legs were not my cup of tea. I was not very optimistic about this third attempt.

I was also obsessed with how Nicole was doing. I was fuming at the idea that she would complete the whole thing in a week. In a nutshell: I am the couch, Nicole is the 5K.

> **Nicole:** *Lauren! Go back and read the chapter on being your own best friend. It's not okay to call yourself a couch!*

You can choose the coach who talks you through the sessions, and I chose Michael Johnson as I found him very encouraging and firm. Being told "Keep going, you're doing grrrrreat" by Michael spurred me on. I felt each time I ran with him in my ears that he was verbally shoving me along.

I did the first run on Christmas Eve. It wasn't fun but, despite my reticence, I did it. I got the thumbs up from some passing neighbours, which was nice; but I also felt fairly pathetic as my husband runs 5K every morning as easily as brushing his teeth, as do my older kids.

I followed the programme to the letter. By day 10 I had completed six runs and was on track. I still had to psych myself up just to leave the front door – I hated it so much. I knew Nicole was highly likely to not stick to the programme and just run five kilometres straight off the bat as she never follows instructions, so I was already annoyed. However, the running itself was keeping me present, which was no bad thing I also felt good when I got home because I had achieved something and had overcome my reluctance.

My waking thought by week four was: "I hate Nicole". The running was destroying me. My left knee was in agony. My lower back was so sore I hadn't run all weekend. I felt guilty and pathetic and frightened of the next week, which consisted of longer runs. It felt insurmountable, but I tried one more run and I managed it. Something that did help me was being invested in what was going on in my ears – it had to be something that engaged me, so I listened to comedy podcasts which kept me distracted.

By day 20 I had completed 10 runs. It was week four and I was doing five-minute runs with no break. For me that was huge progress. That morning, I realised that I would do almost anything to prevent myself from going on a run. I even ironed. The thought of going on the run was so overwhelmingly awful. But I did it. And I felt an enormous sense of achievement. I even filmed myself singing the Rocky theme tune as I ran.

I wish I could tell you that I completed the programme, but I didn't. As the runs got longer, they overwhelmed me and made me cry – and I am not a person who cries easily. I am yet to complete Couch to 5K.

Nicole
I am used to training five times a week in the gym, and my exercise of choice is brutal and challenging – I do a lot of plyometric and explosive work ...

Lauren: Blah blah blah, plyometric ... NOBODY cares!
Nicole: That's a bit mean, but okay.

The point I am (badly) trying to make is I am not a newbie to exercise, and this app is brilliantly designed for people who are. So please keep that in mind before I continue.

The practice started on Christmas Eve. It was cold, wet and possibly the worst time to start an outdoors physical challenge. I chose my narrator (Sanjeev) as I liked the sound of his voice.

The first run went well, I followed the instructions, which is most unlike me. It took 28 minutes and I included a hill run, because when it comes to exercise, I HAVE to be a bit extra. I came home happy and proud.

I knew it was going to annoy Lauren immensely but she was going to have to suck it up as this practice was my lane. She is invested in vaginas and I am invested in physical activity and that's just the way it goes.

Run number two: I didn't bother with the app. I had tried it once, got the idea and remembered I hated being told what to do. I also wanted to test my fitness levels and see how all my gym work translated to running. I managed four kilometres with a bit of walking and, considering how hard I work in the damn gym, this felt a bit disappointing.

By run three I completed the full 5K, and on run four I managed 6K. After a few runs, my knees began to hurt and I remembered why I don't run: my body doesn't like it. I probably did eight runs in total and on a couple of them I failed miserably. On those days my body was sluggish and refused to cooperate, but that's part of the exercise game. You can't always hit PBs, but the trick is to know when to push through and when to allow your body to do what it needs.

Lauren and I had briefly discussed her completing 5K and myself completing 10K, which we both had huge enthusiasm for at the time. But, before you get excited, neither of these things happened.

WHAT DID WE LEARN?
Lauren
I am really under-confident in my body's abilities. I feel my body is capable of so much less that it actually is. The psychological block of "I have to put on my trainers and do something hard that I hate" was always much worse than the run itself. With each run, because the programme was building me up gradually, I knew I could achieve it, yet every day I dreaded it in equal amounts, and this never shifted. However, I did gain a sense of achievement, and when I returned, I felt good about myself.

I wish I had wisdom for you here, but this practice was destined to be one I was not going to complete. I still wish I had. Maybe one day I'll try again. But I'm here representing those for whom running just isn't their thing.

Nicole
I was immediately impressed with the app. It leads you into the running and recovery seamlessly. If you are someone who has never run before, this is the app for you. It's free and foolproof.

I completed the full 5K within three runs, but let me caveat this with the fact that I have trained for many years and taught myself how to mentally cope with pushing my body hard.

Couch to 5K can feel daunting, but it is also really fun and achievable. If your body is healthy then you can eventually run five kilometres – it's your mind you have to convince. Plus, and here's the best part, there is NOTHING like the flood of endorphins after a run. All the pain is worth it for those.

TAKE-AWAY TIPS

Sleep hygiene
Just make one change at a time and see if it can improve your quality of sleep. Start with removing your devices from the bedroom.

Awe walking
You can find awe wherever you are. You just need to set the intention of finding it and there it will be.

Couch to 5K
Make sure you have something great in your ears (preferably an episode of *Self Care Club* podcast) – the more distracted you are, the easier the run.

READER CHALLENGES

Lauren's challenge
Get outside and consciously watch for small wonders in the world around you. Even on a route you take every day there will be something new and special to notice and enjoy.

Nicole's challenge
Download Couch to 5K today! Put on some trainers and go! Don't delay it, because you'll be so proud of yourself. Just remember, in 30 minutes it will be done and you will be basking in the endorphin high.

7

_____

Relationships

Before we jump into this chapter, we want to give some housekeeping rules: have you read Chapter 1 on boundaries? We ask this because having solid boundaries will support every relationship you have in your life: romantic, platonic, professional and the one you have with yourself. Once boundaries are in place, you'll be in a much stronger position to tackle the issues that are likely to arise in your relationships and this chapter. Okay, so now that we know where the emergency exits are, let's begin.

KEY PLAYERS

Ever felt lonely even when you're surrounded by people? Or totally connected and content when you're with just one person? The people we have in our lives dictate the overall *quality* of our lives, and the relationships we invest time and heart into can either add richness or deplete us.

The people we surround ourselves with are the biggest influence on our behaviour, attitudes and our achievements. In the words of motivational speaker Jim Rohn, "You are the average of the five people you spend the most time with." These key players shape who we are. They influence what we're thinking, saying, doing and becoming; they determine what conversations dominate our attention. Research by social psychologist Dr David McClelland of Harvard University found that the people you habitually associate with

175

"determine as much as 95% of your success or failure in life". It is up to all of us to consciously construct our relationships and decide which opinions, attitudes and life philosophies we do and do not allow to be a part of our life.

We only have the bandwidth for a limited number of buddies. In fact, if we subscribe to evolutionary psychologist Robin Dunbar's theory of "Dunbar's number", which he defines as *the number of stable relationships people are cognitively able to maintain at once*, then we all have just five close cry-on-my-shoulder, drop-everything-at-a-moment's-notice friends.

So, if we become like the people we choose to surround ourselves with, how do we ensure we are focusing on investing in the relationships that best serve us? We need to ask some pertinent questions. Who do I spend the most time with? Who are the people who I trust, who support me, who lift me up and who encourage me?

LONELINESS

Despite living in a world where we are constantly connected, we are facing a loneliness epidemic. Statistics suggest that loneliness is becoming increasingly prevalent, particularly in younger generations. According to one 2019 survey from the US, 25% of adults between the ages of 18 and 27 reported having no close friends, while 22% reported having no friends at all. The rise of the internet and, ironically, social media, are partially to blame.

The effects of loneliness have been widely studied and can have dramatic consequences on our physical, mental and emotional health – recent headlines stated that loneliness poses as great a risk to our health as smoking 15 cigarettes a day. Social isolation significantly increases a person's risk of premature death from all causes, a risk that may rival those of smoking, obesity and physical inactivity. It gives about a 50% increased risk of dementia, a 29% increased risk of heart disease and a 32% increased risk of stroke. Loneliness is also associated with higher rates of depression, anxiety and suicide.

So, cultivating and investing in the relationships we have in our lives is vital. It is not about quantity, it is about quality.

> **Lauren:** *This is why we spend all our time together.*
> **Nicole:** *Ahh, I like it when you're soppy.*

Relationships can be born out of many things and not always from the things we expect or want. They can run from a place of duty, obligation, guilt or convenience; or they can be from a place of love, respect, admiration, trust, loyalty and many other values that help elevate us and the other person. Often, we invest our time in relationships that are bad for us and neglect those that offer more joy.

In this chapter, we want to bring awareness to your relationships and point you towards the joyful ones, to help you start to eliminate the ones that drain you, and to give you tools so that both parties can thrive and connect.

Let's start by figuring out who you spend most of your time with, and whether the majority of the relationships you invest in are helping you to thrive or not.

Healthy vs unhealthy relationships

For the following tables, consider any one relationship in your life, and tick the statements that apply.

Signs of a healthy relationship

You feel uplifted after being with them	
You have mutual love between you	
You respect one another	
You trust one another	
You can be your most authentic self	
You can both be vulnerable	
You can be honest with one another	
You laugh together	
You look forward to being with them	
You feel peaceful and calm in the relationship	
You feel it is an equal and reciprocal relationship	
You encourage and admire each other	

Signs of an unhealthy relationship

You feel exhausted/drained when you leave their company	
You don't want to see or speak to them	
You feel guilty when you haven't seen them	
They often give you a hard time	
You feel a sense of duty to keep investing in the relationship	
You feel obligated to see/speak to them	
It is heavily one-sided	
They only call you when they need you	
There is no space for your needs	
You don't feel respected	
You cannot trust them	
You cannot authentically be yourself around them	
Their opinions, attitudes or behaviours make you feel uncomfortable	

If you ticked more from the bottom list than the top, you may want to reassess the relationship and read on.

THE PRACTICES

The practices we have chosen can be used with your relationships with your family, romantic partners, friends and work colleagues.

- **Knowing when to let go**
- **How to have a difficult conversation**

There are other practices that we have loved and found very helpful for relationships but couldn't fit in the book, However, they can be found on our podcast on the following episodes:

- Letting go of being right
- How to give a heartfelt apology
- Active listening
- Assuming good intent
- No complaining (this one's more geared towards romantic relationships)

KNOWING WHEN TO LET GO

You may have heard the phrase "People come into your life for a season, a reason or a lifetime". Not everyone stays in your life forever, and nor should they. As human beings we are meant to evolve and change, and sometimes certain relationships don't last the distance.

Let's be honest: letting go of anything can be hard. Whether it's a relationship that is well past its sell-by date, a job where there is no opportunity for promotion, a bad habit that is detrimental to you, or even that beloved dress that is never going to zip up however hard you breathe in. Removing these things from our lives can signify an ending we may not be ready for, no matter how needed it may be. As humans, we are hardwired to hang in there. We are all more likely to stay long past the expiry date of a situation or relationship than we are to bail out prematurely.

Letting go of something that is no longer serving you is categorically a healthy decision. For example, letting go of a toxic relationship where you always feel unseen and walked over is a positive stance to take in your life. Letting go of a job you hate in order to move on to a job you love will help you move forwards. We are talking about the empowering side of letting go, which is a vital step in moving towards the next chosen stage of your life.

Unfun Fact

This practice is not a permission slip to quit or walk away from things that may feel hard or push you out of your comfort zone. This is about the areas of your life where you feel drained, stressed or that have stopped serving you in some way. Knowing the difference is the important part which we are going to uncover here.

THE SUNK COST FALLACY

When you have invested time, money and energy into something it feels very hard to just drop it. There is even a name for this: the "sunk cost fallacy". If you've invested £10,000 of savings into your milkshake business, built a website and spent hours curating your Instagram feed but your milkshakes ain't bringing any boys to the yard and it's all going sour and clearly failing, then it's going to be extremely hard to simply let it go.

Human beings are wired to be both optimistic and loss averse. What this means in real terms is that you may be in a shitty job or a toxic relationship, which deep down you know you should leave, but from time to time, you get some unpredictable rewards. Maybe your vile boss gives you the afternoon off or gives you a compliment about your contributions in a meeting, or maybe your emotionally absent partner suddenly comes home with flowers. You can suddenly start questioning if it's really all so bad or if it's actually just all fine and choose to stay longer.

As Kylie said, it's better the devil you know. We are no different from the rats in behavioural psychologist BF Skinner's experiment. Skinner discovered that when rats pushed a lever for food and were rewarded some of the time (but not every time or none of the time) the rats would try even harder for longer. Like them, we may be in a bad situation in which we are occasionally thrown a bone, and therefore perceive it as something worth continuing with.

Signs that it might be time to let go

For the following table, consider any relationship, job, "thing", etc., and tick the statements that apply to it.

You feel emotionally unattached to whatever it is: the relationship, the job, the "thing"	
It makes you constantly stressed or unhappy	
It causes anxiety and/or overwhelm more than it should	
You can't see any room for growth or improvement	
You feel annoyed that you have to spend time on it or with that person	
You feel stuck	
You feel suffocated	
The cons are outweighing the pros	
You feel relief when you give yourself permission to consider not doing it anymore or not being around that person	

How many did you tick? Is it time to do an Elsa?

Lauren: *An Elsa?*

Nicole: *I forget, you have sons. Frozen? Let it go? It won an Oscar ... Oh never mind.*

BENEFITS OF LETTING GO

When you choose to let go of things that don't serve you:

- Are choosing to prioritise yourself
- Create possibility
- Are opening yourself up for new experiences and opportunities
- Grow as a person
- Learn to recognise the things that do not serve you anymore
- Focus your time and energy on things and people that uplift you and bring abundance to your life

SELF-CARE STEPS FOR KNOWING WHEN TO LET GO

Letting go of something that isn't good for you takes courage and self-awareness and we know how difficult that can be. Here are some factors to consider when determining if it's time.

Step 1: Evaluate your wellbeing

Reflect on how the situation or activity is affecting your overall wellbeing. Are you experiencing excessive stress, anxiety or negative emotions? Does it take a toll on your physical health or mental state? If it constantly undermines your wellbeing, it may be a sign that it's time to "do an Elsa".

Step 2: Assess your values and goals

Consider whether the situation aligns with your values and long-term goals. Does it contradict your core beliefs or hinder your progress towards personal or professional aspirations?

Step 3: Analyse the costs and benefits

Weigh the pros and cons of continuing with the situation. Consider the potential benefits and the drawbacks. If the negative aspects significantly outweigh the positives, it might be a clear signal that letting it go is the right choice.

Step 4: Trust your intuition

Pay attention to your gut feelings and instincts. Sometimes, your intuition can guide you towards what is genuinely best for you. If you have a persistent sense of unease or a strong inner voice telling you to quit, it's worth listening to.

Step 5: Seek support and advice

Talk to trusted friends, family or mentors who can provide an outside and more objective perspective. Share your concerns and gather their insights. They may offer valuable advice or perspectives that can help you make an informed decision.

OUR EXPERIENCE

Lauren

I had been doing the podcast for two years while simultaneously working as a birth doula (which I had done for 16 years). The service I offered to my clients involved meetings to prepare for the birth, unlimited contact via phone/email throughout the pregnancy, being "on-call" 24 hours a day, seven days a week for the final month of the pregnancy, and then in-person continuous emotional and physical support through the labour and birth – however long the birth may take. My role was to provide nurturing, continuous support and reassurance. It is an honour and a privilege to be invited to bear witness at the everyday miracle of birth. Having a baby is something that we only get to do a handful of times if we are lucky. I took the responsibility very seriously.

Being a doula is not a job you can dial into. You have to connect and care. And there is no getting around the fact that babies come when they choose, which is usually many days late, usually at 3am and just when I had a wedding or birthday to attend, when my husband was on a work trip abroad or when I had nobody to help with school pick up. The unavoidable unpredictability of the work became second nature. I answered every invitation with "If I'm not at a birth" and everyone understood. I was almost constantly on-call and having to leave at the drop of a hat when "the call" came. It never got any easier, regardless of my experience.

The podcast recordings were scheduled in: we had a writing and recording routine, and I arranged my meetings around Nicole's work days. But our week was disrupted whenever I had to leave to attend a birth. I couldn't give Nicole any forward notice and I needed recovery time when I returned. It was becoming inconvenient and hard to juggle both and give both my full attention.

I was also getting tired. I was past the childbearing years of my life, and as my years of being mummy to a baby faded, so did my passion. I became very discerning with who I agreed to take on. I resented having to go out on cold dark evenings to meetings. I became grumpy about not having any control over my time and energy. But I could not let it go.

Going through the self-care steps outlined above I realised continuing my work as a doula was taking a toll and undermining my wellbeing. I was having negative feelings. Being a doula was no longer aligning with my goals and professional ambitions, which was to grow the podcast.

I weighed up the costs and benefits: the money was regular, I was good at it, it was what I knew; but my instinct was telling me strongly that it was time to retire. Nicole then retired from hairdressing. It was a huge moment for her, and it also put the pressure on me to think about why I was unable to do the same. I felt like I was being unfair to Nicole, but I was scared. I also knew it was wrong to do this work without my full heart in it, and that until I took that leap of faith, Nicole and I were not going to progress in the way we wanted to.

For the first time ever, I started to turn away enquiries. Nicole waited patiently for me to finish with the clients I had already committed to. I told my last client that their baby's birth would be the last I attended and it was bittersweet. The birth itself was perfect, and I was so grateful to have left on such a high. It took me a few months more to cancel my membership to my organisational body, which felt like the last tie I had to the role; but it was surprisingly uneventful. I felt no sadness, only the conviction that I was letting go of something that no longer served me in order to make space for something else that I truly wanted for myself.

I can honestly say that as much as I look back now with great fondness on my time as a doula and I'm proud of what I achieved, I also know that it was time to let it go. (The cold never bothered me anyway.)

Nicole

I was in a friendship with a woman – let's call her "Lucy" – that had turned a bit sour.

Lucy and I were very close and we spent lots of time together as families. We went on holidays, we would spend Christmas together, our kids were best friends (they went to the same schools), and she even worked for my husband. Our lives were completely intertwined.

I had started training as a coach. I was growing and learning about myself at a rapid rate. The more I was coming into myself and finding my voice and using it, the more I noticed a subtle shift in attitude from her.

I don't know why, but Lucy began behaving ever so slightly differently towards me. She stopped commenting on my Facebook posts, when normally she always would; we were seeing one another less; I got the sense that I wasn't allowed to speak about my new work, and felt very edited in her presence. Call it intuition, or whatever you want, but my good friend felt very distant and I had got to the point of total bemusement and frustration.

While doing her hair one Saturday afternoon, I decided to ask her about it. This was one of the closest people in my life, so it felt like the most natural thing to do. I asked her what was going on and she completely shut down on me. She refused to answer and went silent. Every time I pressed her on it, she remained muted, as if I hadn't spoken. I was completely bewildered. I carried on doing her hair in total silence, the tension was so thick I could've blunted my scissors on the energy in that room. She left my salon without saying a word. I couldn't get my head around what had happened, and I felt pretty heartbroken that I couldn't have a simple honest chat with someone I loved.

A few days later we were due to see one another at school sports day. I texted her: "I'm aware I'm seeing you later and we haven't spoken but wanted to check if everything was okay?"

FYI: this was a red flag. I was prioritising her needs, even though she had hurt me, and I was the one needing to smooth it over and neglect myself.

She replied: "I don't know what you are on about, everything is fine."

Another red flag – total denial that anything seismic had happened.

Everything returned to "normal", with this brand-new elephant in the room. I felt scared to bring it back up, not wanting a repeat performance, but it was such a disregard and disrespect to my needs in the relationship. All I wanted was to discuss any difficulties that might be present, hear one another and move on, but I knew I wasn't going to get anywhere. She made it very clear we were not to discuss it. Wanting to keep everything nice, I reluctantly followed her lead.

We went on a summer holiday together, which unsurprisingly I found very difficult. November came around and the relationship, for me, had become intolerable. Lucy would subtly do and say things that would knock me down, she refused to engage with the coach/podcast part of me, and limited me to a box that was convenient for her. Or so it seemed, I'm sure she would have another side to the story.

In a nutshell, I felt I had to behave in a certain way to keep her happy – which was small, quiet and passive. Not exactly on brand.

After a dinner together where we were with another couple, I watched her engage with the other woman and show overt interest in her life, all the while ignoring me. It all felt very intentional, very childish and very unkind.

The next day, I decided to try talking to her again and texted asking if she would meet me for a coffee.

Her reply was: "Your thoughts and feelings are of no interest to me."

I immediately called her; she blocked my call. In that moment, I knew our friendship was over. She chose to end our friendship rather than have an honest conversation. To this day I will never understand it. I was left *utterly heartbroken. What happened after that was beyond unpleasant as our intertwined lives imploded. We never spoke again.*

Five weeks later, I met Lauren. I always call her my gift.

WHAT DID WE LEARN?
Lauren

When you let go of something you are actually making space in the universe for something else. When you are tied up with something that physically or energetically isn't serving you, it is blocking you from receiving something better. We both found, almost immediately upon quitting our jobs in hairdressing and doula work, that the podcast took off in ways we could not have imagined.

Nicole

The relationship with Lucy was only allowed to exist on her terms, which by my standards were simply not workable. The moment I asked for simple honesty the relationship fell apart. I am grateful for the experience, as I learnt what a healthy, respectful relationship should look like. (Which, by the way, never involves being shut down or silenced.) This experience has enriched every friendship in my life since.

Regardless of what happened and the heartbreak it caused, I am proud I listened to my inner voice that was warning me the relationship was not right, and to this day I am pleased she is no longer in my life. She didn't deserve a seat at my table. It was a hard lesson, but a life-changing one.

Meeting Lauren soon after was a beautiful sign that once you let go of something that is not serving you, the other side is full of something far more nourishing. I let go of a friendship filled with difficulty, envy and limitations, and found a friendship where I get to show up and be celebrated as the fullest version of myself.

HOW TO HAVE A DIFFICULT CONVERSATION

Nobody enjoys having a difficult conversation, but they are necessary in order to be able to function with integrity and to develop respectful, long-lasting relationships. In this practice, we will hold your hand as we tiptoe through navigating how to have that difficult conversation you never thought you could have.

Sometimes we are faced with a challenging situation where a tricky conversation is needed. You may need to end a romantic relationship, or perhaps a friend or work colleague has upset you. As much as we desperately want to avoid it, there are times when a difficult conversation is unavoidable, even when it makes us anxious, stressed and want to sprint in the opposite direction.

Most people don't enjoy confrontation. They find it daunting and frightening, and would rather avoid it with a ten-foot barge pole and live with the upset they are carrying around. But the good news is, having a difficult conversation is not about confrontation – it's about finding resolution.

Carrying around hurt feelings or regrets about relationships that are struggling is a heavy weight to bear, so rather than allowing things to fester and a relationship to haemorrhage, it's far better for your overall wellbeing to be brave and initiate a conversation. If you tackle the conversation in the right way, it can help the other person better understand your feelings and beliefs, and may even improve the situation or relationship. It's an investment in a relationship to be able to say that you value someone enough to want to talk things through.

Each difficult conversation is an opportunity to learn. As soon as you start a conversation that gets you talking to another person, you learn about yourself, about them, and you grow as a person.

Karamo Brown from *Queer Eye* (one of our favourite feel-good shows) gives the great advice that before you even start a dialogue make sure that you can answer these four questions for yourself:

- *Can I be responsive instead of reactive?*
- *How do I hope this conversion will help me grow?*
- *How do I hope this conversation will help the other person grow?*
- *What do I hope will be the end result of this conversation?*

Before you even have the conversation, there are some things that need to be put into place.

- **Think of it as a way to find resolution and peace**. This isn't about apportioning blame or creating conflict.
- **Find the right time and the right place**. Don't confront someone in a busy public space. Find a quiet, neutral space where you both feel comfortable speaking openly.
- **Be direct and give warning**. Don't ambush anyone into the conversation without any pre-warning. It's unfair. Give them time and notice that you would like to talk to them about something and, if applicable, give them an outline of what the issue is without going into it.
- **Make sure you are not hungry, thirsty, overtired or feeling very hormonal**. Those things can really (badly) impact how you show up and present yourself. At the risk of sounding like the Jewish mothers we are: eat something first!

So, here we are, feeling brave and at the agreed time in a neutral space. How do we go about the conversation?

SELF-CARE STEPS ON HOW TO HAVE A DIFFICULT CONVERSATION

Step 1: Impact

Think about what impact you want the conversation to have. Anticipate the resolution before you begin, have a goal in mind and be positive and expectant about the outcome. If you go in thinking, "This is going to be a disaster", then it's likely that it will be. Focus on the outcome, and stay connected to that throughout the conversation.

Step 2: Show respect and vulnerability

Even when the subject matter is difficult, conversations can remain mutually supportive. Be respectful of the other person. Respect their point of view and expect the same in return. Allow yourself to be honest and vulnerable and you may find they are too. It's perfectly okay to say, "I'm feeling nervous" or, "I'm finding it uncomfortable" or, "This isn't easy for me". Humanise it for both of you.

Step 3: Plan what you are going to say

A big part of tackling difficult conversations is communicating clearly and directly. It's a good idea to plan what you want to say beforehand so that your nerves or emotions don't get the better of you. This way you can be sure that you make all the points you want to, rather than allowing the conversation to divert or forgetting something you later realise was important. You can come prepared with notes to support you in this.

Step 4: Use "I" statements

Start by explaining how *you* feel, what *you* think and why. Keep it as your own experience, rather than accusing someone else and throwing blame. Take ownership of your feelings. Try not to use statements that begin with "You", as this can make the other person feel attacked and defensive;

instead, use "I" statements. For example, instead of saying, "You don't care about my feelings", try, "I felt really upset when ..."

Step 5: Describe the outcome you want

Do you want an apology, an acknowledgement of what has happened or for them to behave differently in the future? Tell them! This will help them see things from your point of view and give them a clear way forward by knowing what your intentions and hopes are for the conversation.

Step 6: Come with sincere curiosity

Ask *why* this issue is happening instead of accusing someone of something. The point of this conversation is to learn why the other person is behaving in a way that is having a negative impact on you and your relationship.

Step 7: Actively listen

You may have spent days, weeks or even months going over all the sarcastic, witty, sharp comebacks that you wish you had said at the time of the incident. As satisfying as they may seem to you, this is not the place for them. If you are instigating a challenging conversation, your job is to listen fully and to allow the other person to respond. Don't spend the time when the other person is talking thinking about what you want to say next. Really listen to what they're saying. Try to understand their point of view. Ask them questions like "Can you tell me more about that?" or "How does that make you feel?" Don't talk over them. You may learn something about them that you didn't know or see the situation from a different angle. If they see that you're switched on and engaged with them, then they're more likely to do the same for you.

Step 8: Let go of the need to be right

Being right can be the most seductive thing in the world, but rarely does it bring resolve and it usually adds more conflict. If you can let go of this need that you are right and they are wrong, the conversation will be much more successful.

Step 9: Perspective

Try to see the situation from their perspective: has this person done/ said anything like this before, or is this totally out of character? Is there anything else going on in their life that might be a factor? Did you do anything that may have hurt/confused/angered them that might account for what's happened? People do and say things for many different reasons. Remember, it's not always about you!

FALL-OUT

As we live in the real world, sadly not everything ends with you saying your piece, them saying theirs, and then skipping off into the sunset holding hands; so it's important to discuss what to do if the worst happens and the conversation doesn't go well.

Sometimes you can do everything in your power to have a constructive chat, but if the other person isn't willing to do the same, it can feel like it's going nowhere. So here are a few options if the other person is too upset, angry or emotional to respond.

- **Take a break**. Walk away and try again when you've both had time to calm down. Agree to come back later if there is more to say.
- **Agree to disagree**. Not all conversations like this are going to have a happy ending and that's okay. Agreeing to disagree doesn't mean you are backing down. What you are doing is protecting yourself by choosing which battles to fight. As we learnt from the first practice in this chapter, knowing when to let go is powerful.
- **Be patient**. Sometimes it may take a few conversations for you both to be heard and understood – not everything has to be resolved immediately. Allow for space and time around this.

- **Look after yourself**. Difficult conversations like this can sometimes get a bit heated as emotions, hurt or anger are expressed. You may feel drained, relieved or upset. Taking care of yourself afterwards is a priority. Take time to switch off and relax. Go for a walk, listen to a podcast or some music, meditate, or talk to someone who makes you feel good.

Fun Fact

You get to be proud of yourself for starting this conversation. This is hard and takes real courage.

WHAT IF THE SITUATION IS REVERSED?

What if you find yourself on the receiving end of somebody trying to initiate a difficult conversation with you? (Ouch.) Well, the same rules apply.

If you are ambushed and are not expecting the conversation and you don't feel comfortable or ready to engage in it, then be direct and honest and say that. Don't deflect it. It's perfectly okay to say that now is not the right time, but you are happy to arrange another time to talk. If the other person cannot be respectful, is aggressive or replies with sarcasm or comebacks, then politely let them know that their lack of respect is not okay with you and tell them you are walking away. When you finally do have the conversation, allow the other person to say their piece and listen carefully before responding. Author and motivational speaker Simon Sinek says he lets everyone else in the room speak first so he knows exactly what's in the room; he can then respond appropriately to what's in the space.

OUR EXPERIENCE

Lauren

The most difficult conversation I have ever had was the culmination of a long-standing situation at work where I was being discriminated against for fertility issues by someone I was very close to. It had grown increasingly toxic, as other people in the workspace had become involved and were privy to all the details. I found out via a leaked email that internal conversations had been going on behind my back, but I was too intimidated and fearful to speak up. I was consumed by this daily. It took up so much space in my head, it drained me and it was affecting my day-to-day mood.

The whole situation, which had been ongoing for three years, escalated as an annual appraisal and pay review approached. I spent the evening before worrying and feeling incredibly resentful. During the review, it became clear that we were not going to be able to resolve this by ourselves. A very difficult conversation needed to be had and it was going to be impossible without mediation. The mediator we chose was someone in the company who we both liked and trusted and was completely objective.

Shortly before the scheduled meeting, I called the mediator to say I could not do it. I listed all the reasons I couldn't have this difficult conversation. She listened and convinced me to attend. She said that I needed to say my piece and tell my side of the story, as carrying around this weight was negatively impacting my life.

On the morning of the meeting, I made notes so that I could be sure that I didn't forget everything that I wanted to address, as I felt so sure I would be waylaid by emotion and distracted. We met in a quiet, neutral, familiar space. Going into it, I felt sick with nerves – I was uncomfortable and emotional, angry and anxious. The mediator asked me to speak first. I felt embarrassed as I got out my notes and explained why I needed them. I calmly made my points. I got everything out that I needed to. My upset, my hurt, all the things that I had been repressing and holding on to for years.

I quickly realised that this was my opportunity to be able to speak in a safe space. I was really interested in how we could find some form of resolution, but as the conversation progressed, it became clear that wasn't possible. Regardless of this, I found the act of having the conversation so cathartic that it changed everything for me. They listened and were respectful when I spoke; I wasn't interrupted or told I was wrong. They took it all in and took full accountability for my hurt. I felt heard for the first time and able to share the impact it had on me. Afterwards I was exhausted, and despite us not having an ideal outcome I felt lighter. I also felt proud of myself for finally being able to say all the things I had been bottling up for so long.

Nicole

I wish I could tell you that this practice was a breeze, but it's my worst nightmare, as sometimes I really struggle to express myself.

Remember "Lucy" from the previous practice? Well, a few months after she told me that my thoughts and feelings didn't matter, we somehow managed to arrange a meeting to discuss the fall out. I barely ate or slept in the days leading up to it; all I wanted was some sort of resolve and to repair our broken friendship.

We arranged to meet in the neutral space of a café one Sunday morning. I arrived first and sat facing the door. She arrived shortly after and, as she came in, her facial expression told me everything. She was angry, and it instantly dominated the mood. I was hoping for openness, but I could sense she wasn't bringing that to the table.

She nervously tried to make small talk and I politely replied with, "Let's just talk about what we need to." She didn't like that, but my nerves were getting the better of me. My heart was pounding out of my chest and I couldn't think straight. She pulled out a pile of notes and slammed them on the table. As she began with point one, I said, "How many of these are there?" With that, she stood up and stormed out.

I called after her, she ignored me; I called her phone, she blocked the call; I sent numerous texts, all of which were ignored. In desperation, I called her husband and he told me she wasn't returning to the café. I was heartbroken – for the second time by the same person.

I had waited weeks for this conversation with great anticipation and hope, and it lasted a full three minutes with zero resolve. I am sharing this story because I often look back at this day and try to understand how I could've handled things differently.

With hindsight and a broader education on how these conversations can be more successful, I see where I went wrong. Firstly, my nerves intervened and I behaved in a way I wish I hadn't. I should have come in with an open heart and space for her to say what she needed to say. But, in truth, even if I had done so and followed each step mentioned in this practice, the conversation probably would have ended in the same way, simply because we both came to the meeting with different agendas. She came to prove my wrongdoings, and I came hoping to find some peace.

WHAT DID WE LEARN?
Lauren
You need to go into a difficult conversation with the intention of it being a constructive conversation. It's not a place to hurl stones. Whether or not you can find resolution, it's important to have the intention to move forwards in some way if you want to be in a relationship with the other

person. Even if you can't achieve that, there is satisfaction in knowing that you have tried. There is also a relief and a freedom to be found in simply having the conversation. The worst bit is the stuff you are holding on to. The outcome or resolution could make you feel much better than you do now, so it's worth taking the risk, however anxiety-provoking that is.

Nicole
The biggest thing I learnt is that to have a successful conversation, both parties have to be open to hearing one another in the hope of finding resolve.

I had my "speech" prepared, but that was the wrong approach. I needed to see it as an opportunity to learn how she perceived the fall out and hear what she had to say. Hindsight has taught me it was too early for us to have the conversation, and perhaps if we had waited a few more weeks, we may have found a way back to our friendship. I see now that I was still too hurt to get past that long enough to consider Lucy's feelings.

TAKE-AWAY TIPS

Knowing when to let go
Knowing when to let go is a powerful stance to take. Think of it as a way of bringing possibility into your life instead of something negative. Really tune into your body when it feels out of sorts – it is giving you information to help support you.

How to have a difficult conversation
This is not a confrontation or a way to start conflict – it's an act of respect. Keep it solution-focused.

READER CHALLENGES

Lauren's challenge

If you want or need to have a difficult conversation but are not yet ready to put it into action, get yourself prepared by making some notes. It will make everything clear in your head, and you will hopefully feel armed to take the next step.

Nicole's challenge

Go back to the checklist at the beginning of this chapter and consider each important relationship in your life; decide which are healthy and which are not. Once you have that, start to think about what might need to change in order for those relationships to work better for you and the other person.

8

Work–Life Balance

Work–life balance refers to a state of equilibrium where you prioritise your time and energy between your job or career and the other aspects of your life, such as your family, social life, personal interests, and your health and wellbeing. It's not about splitting your time 50/50 between work and leisure, but making sure you feel fulfilled and content in all areas of your life.

In today's fast-paced and competitive work environment, striking a balance can feel like a Sisyphean task. The demands and to-do lists are endless, and it can seem like once we thrive in one area, it leaves others in disarray.

HOW WE WORK

In this post-pandemic era we are still figuring out new arrangements around how we work. The "new normal" challenges traditional relationships between employers and employees, and our time spent at work and where we work; all of which has an impact on our work–life balance. We collectively craved more balance, and while Covid-19 had devastating effects, it gave us the chance to question how and where we wanted to work.

Some companies now offer the option of remote working, some have adopted a hybrid model, while others are back in the office full time. What is clear is that the line between work and home has blurred. Remote working has increased flexibility and reduced commute times for some people, and 86% of people feel that working remotely reduces their stress levels and has helped them save money. However, others who work remotely find it difficult to maintain a healthy work–life balance due to there being no physical separation between home and office. According to a survey, 65% of people admit that now that they work remotely, they are working longer hours than ever before.

Society has normalised (sometimes celebrated) working long hours, answering emails and messages long after the end of the working day. It has, at times, become a bit of a status symbol to boast about how exhausted we are and how hard we are working. This may be a seductive default, but it is simply not good for our overall wellbeing.

This chapter explores some ideas on ways to stay sane in the working world.

BURNOUT

When our work–life balance is out of kilter it can be detrimental to our health. It leaves us stressed and anxious, and it harms performance and productivity at work. It can lead to obesity, cardiovascular disease and poor sleep, as well as increase the risk of mental health problems such as depression and anxiety. It can be the cause of burnout, which is complete physical, mental and emotional exhaustion. Having poor work–life balance strains relationships with family and friends with a lack of time to spend with them, or simply being too tired or stressed to engage positively. In the words of Dolly Parton, "Never get so busy making a living that you forget to make a life."

Let's look at whether or not you are experiencing potential burnout. Here are some common warning signs.

Common signs of burnout

For the following table, tick all the statements that apply to you.

You are always tired	
Your body is always in pain	
You suffer with disturbed sleep	
You have limited patience	
You've lost interest in your job	
You don't look after yourself (#selfcare)	
You're glued to your phone or laptop	
You suffer with self-doubt	
You feel disengaged	
You are unproductive	

How many did you tick?

We know that it's not always possible to make changes at work. For example, if you're on a zero-hours contract you might not feel comfortable speaking up; you might need to work long shifts to earn enough money to pay your bills; or you might be self-employed. There is no one-size-fits-all solution here, so finding a balance that works for your unique situation is vital.

This chapter will point you towards what you *can* do, not what you can't; there will always be strategies and ways to help you manage that bit better, even when it feels impossible.

Always start with a quick check-in with yourself; this will help and inform you about where you're at and what you might need.

1. **Pause**. Ask yourself: What's currently causing me stress or unhappiness? How is that affecting the quality of my life? What am

I losing out on? We often don't take the time to take a step back and reflect on how we are doing until a major life event forces us to re-evaluate.

2. **Pay attention to your feelings**. Are you fulfilled and happy, or angry and resentful? Ask yourself: Do I want to continue to feel this way? How do I want to feel?

3. **Reprioritise**. Think about what it is that you would like to change. Sometimes just taking that time to consider what you want to shift can be a life-changing moment as it moves you from being stuck and trapped – into possibility.

4. **Consider your options**. Is there anything at work or home you can change to meet your new priorities?

Fun Fact

This quick check-in process works in every other area of your life, too.

THE PRACTICES

- **Fika**
- **Work smart**
- **Asking for help**

There are many other strategies that you can use to help you achieve this balance, including establishing boundaries between work and personal life and learning to say "No" (see Chapter 1, Boundaries); learning how to have a difficult conversation (see Chapter 7, Relationships); asking for what you want (see Chapter 3, Confidence); taking breaks and holidays and engaging in activities outside of work that promote physical and mental health (see Chapter 6, Physical Health).

FIKA

Once upon a time, we were all hot for *hygge* (pronounced "hue-gah"), the Danish concept that made staying in and being cozy cool. Then along came *niksen* – the Dutch art of doing nothing. This was followed by *koselig* from Norway – sort of *hygge* v2.0, but more focused on the social aspect and being outdoors.

Well now there is *fika* (from Sweden), and it could be exactly what you need to help your work–life balance. (In the UK we seem to look to the culture of our Northern European friends for ideas about how to get off the hamster wheel for a moment and enjoy the simpler things in life.)

Fika is often translated as "a coffee and cake break", but it's more important than that. Many Swedes consider it essential to make time for *fika* every day. It means making time for friends and colleagues to share a cup of coffee and a little snack. *Fika* is a ritual, a concept, a state of mind, an attitude and an important part of Swedish culture.

The word itself is both a noun and a verb, and is believed to be a reversal of the syllables in the word *kaffi*, the old spelling of coffee. Originally, it was the coffee itself, introduced in Sweden in the 18th century, that was considered the actual *fika*. But, over the years, the accompanying baked treats, called *fikabröd*, became just as important, along with the social aspect of the custom. The arrival of patisseries in Sweden in the 19th century cemented the tradition as a coffee-and-cake custom enjoyed with friends.

All Swedes consider it important to make time to stop and socialise: to pause. It refreshes the brain and strengthens relationships. And it makes good business sense; companies where *fika* is institutionalised are more productive. The Volvo factory plant in Sweden takes *fika* breaks and IKEA talks about it on its website, saying, "More than a coffee break, *fika* is a time to share, connect and relax with colleagues. Some of the best ideas and decisions happen at *fika*."

It's also flexible – you can *fika* outdoors if the weather is good; you can *fika* with one or more friends, or with colleagues – you can even *fika* alone.

BENEFITS OF *FIKA*

Practising *fika* can bring:

- A positive moment of respite in our overloaded, hectic days
- Better connections and conversations; you don't focus on work during *fika*
- Improved productivity and creativity when you're back at your desk

SELF-CARE STEPS TO *FIKA*

Step 1: Take two 10–30-minute breaks throughout your day to reconnect to yourself and others

A cup of coffee is pretty essential, but if you don't drink it then any other drink you enjoy is fine. Most people also combine their break with a sugary pastry, such as a cinnamon bun.

That's it! You are all set. Enjoy!

OUR EXPERIENCE

Lauren

The week we tried fika was hectic. I had been back-to-back with Zoom meetings and gone straight from working all day to picking up the kids and home to cook dinner. It felt completely necessary to fika. I walked into this task with zero hesitation. You had me at cinnamon bun.

I was making a mental list of people I would like to fika with, when my friend and neighbour Karen arrived on my doorstep with her little girl who wanted to see Barker and give him a pat. She said, "I haven't seen you for ages." Grabbing the opportunity that had just presented itself to me, I said, "Karen, do you want to fika with me?" She looked alarmed. I quickly explained it was a catch up over a coffee and pastry, and her eyes lit up. We made a time and date, and I was very much looking forward to it. I arrived at Karen's on the allotted day, and to my delight found that she had been to a local patisserie and bought a selection of goods. We had a lovely time catching up and connecting. I went home feeling full in both my soul and my belly.

I then had a flurry of WhatsApp exchanges with my best friend Kathryn. We just couldn't seem to find time to have a proper chat and finally managed a meagre five minutes on the phone. It had to be addressed. "Kathryn," I said, "Do you want to fika with me?" She said, "I have absolutely no idea what that is, but you know I'll do anything with you, so yes." Much like me, there is not much Kathryn won't do for a cinnamon bun. Although she was swamped with work and I was on-call for a birth, we decided on balance that being together was the most important thing. We arranged to do a Fika Friday. But the fika was scuppered as I was called to a birth overnight and left in desperate need of some freaking fika-ing sleep.

A few days later, I texted Eliza, my sister-in-law: "Hello, do you want to fika with me?"

"Excuse me?"

"Make like a Swede and just say yes. I promise it's not horrible and we already fika all the time."

"What am I getting myself involved in here? Does it involve vaginas?"

A fair comment. But once I explained the concept, she was very much up for it.

Nicole

It may sound like an easy practice, but pausing, although very needed, is something I struggle to achieve comfortably. I had a feeling this probably wasn't my best mode of self-care. I am also not a pastry lover, so I was worried.

I had lots of questions. Tea, coffee, ginger shots? How long do I have to sit there? Do I have to sip the drink slowly or can I chug it down and get on with my day? Can I walk? Do I have to eat something? It felt like a lot of rules. (Lauren informed me that a ginger shot wasn't part of fika and I should sit the fuck down, order a cappuccino and chill out. Bit harsh!) The answer to all of my questions was, whatever allows you to pause and take a moment.

My husband and I went to the gym early one morning on fika week and we were on our way home by 7.45am. I asked him if he fancied a fika. His eyes lit up like a little boy on Christmas morning. I quickly informed him what fika was, and we came home, made a coffee and sat with one another for 15 minutes. No emails, no washing, just coffee and being together on a Tuesday morning. It was lovely, he even made a joke and thanked me for some great fika.

The next day after a workout, I asked my gym girls if they wanted to fika, I explained it was coffee and cake. They didn't like the cake part post-workout, so I used more appropriate "gym" language and we went for green tea and ginger shots.

Lauren: It's good you have these people.

Nicole: *You only say that so I don't drive you mad to do these things.*
Lauren: *Exactly.*

I love my gym girls.

WHAT DID WE LEARN?
Lauren
Two fika breaks a day in your working week could mean 10 pastries a week. Even for me, with my cinnamon bun addiction, it's a lot. Nevertheless, fika is a great excuse to take a little bit of time out to catch up with people properly. I think this is vital to our wellbeing and to feeling connected.

Nicole
I feel very guilty pausing and stopping. I understand the importance of it, but I always prefer to be on the move. I love chatting with the people I love; I just don't need rules around what to eat and drink and for how long. But if you are in an office and/or on a screen all day, I think fika is a necessary practice.

WORK SMART

Do you ever feel like your to-do list is as long as your arm, and by 5pm you feel it's no shorter? We do too – all the time. That's when we discovered a practice called "Work Smart, Not Hard". This practice encourages you to use your energy and time at work more efficiently.

Your time and energy are two of the most precious resources you have, and learning how to manage them is a life skill. We are going to suggest strategies to help you prioritise your work, identify the most important tasks on that never-ending to-do list, and get it all done with some headspace and energy to spare. You're welcome!

BENEFITS OF WORKING SMART

Working smarter not harder can:

- Save energy – working in short bursts, for example, allows you to accomplish challenging tasks with more energy and better results
- Increase your motivation – it can create feelings of positivity about your job, colleagues and yourself
- Create more balance – when working efficiently, you may have more time and energy for other activities

SELF-CARE STEPS TO WORK SMART

Step 1: Prioritise

Decide what the most important and urgent things are on your to-do list, and put them in order of most important to least important.

Step 2: Make meetings productive

As the saying goes: a meeting is an event at which the minutes are kept and the hours are lost. Meetings are often unnecessary, and most go on too long. They suck up time and energy. If you have to go into one, do so with a clear agenda and keep it short, focused and productive. Finish with an action plan and a follow-up date.

Step 3: Focus on one task at a time

Moving from one task to another without completing the first can waste time, as your brain may need time to change its focus. Focus your attention on one task until it's complete or you reach a natural stopping point.

Step 4: Say "no" to unnecessary tasks

Figure out what needs to be done and say "no" to the rest. If you need more help on this, see the How to say "no" practice in Chapter 1, Boundaries.

Step 5: Put your phone on silent/turn off notifications/ take off your smart watch

You don't need us to tell you that the constant pinging on your wrist, phone and laptop is going to affect your concentration levels.

Step 6: Consider taking a break when appropriate (*fika!*)

Consider taking a walk at lunch or a break when you feel it necessary. Even 10 minutes of fresh air and a stretch of your legs will make a difference. This will help improve concentration and energy levels and set you up better for the rest of the day. Try to avoid looking at screens during this break.

OUR EXPERIENCE

Lauren

My weekly workload already consists of researching and writing the shows, recording the podcast, doing the finance admin, general admin (for both work and home), replying to emails and messages and writing this book. Let's add into the mix three children, a dog and a house – all of which need looking after, organising and managing. Suffice to say, I had plenty to be getting on with.

Then thrown into the mix was an opportunity to interview a woman for the podcast who I admire very much. We were going to talk to her about her upcoming book. Her PR team sent us a couple of advance copies and, as I am the reader out of the two of us, I took it upon myself to get stuck in. I read on the tube, I read in bed, I read in the bath. Anytime I was sitting or lying down I had my head stuck in her book, desperately trying to find the time to read it all before the interview. I felt compelled and obliged to do my due diligence with our guest.

She is an extremely accomplished woman who had held high-powered jobs in fashion while simultaneously raising four children, writing two books and hosting a podcast. I was fairly intimidated and reluctant to come across as unprofessionally unprepared. As the week progressed, I highlighted paragraphs, copied quotes and made notes in advance of the interview. I researched her online, I listened to her podcast and others she had guested on such was my concern about being fully prepped. This all took a toll on the many other work tasks that also needed to be done, and by the weekend I was still behind, so I spent six hours on Sunday catching up and having no downtime.

It did not occur to me for one moment that perhaps the author herself, who wrote all of the words and knew she was going to be coming on our show (among others) to promote her book, would be fully aware of all the content and that she would be prepared and ready to share with us.

The morning of the interview arrived. We met on Zoom and, of course, after asking the first simple question of "What's your new book about?", a natural conversation ensued whereby she highlighted the key points and expanded them with anecdotes. Of the 12 questions and many quotes I had prepped, we used none of them. We ended up saying very little as she did all the talking. It was a great interview, and afterwards I realised that just reading her book would have been enough prep work. I had done the very opposite of working smart. Lesson learnt.

Nicole

The practice week began with our video editor telling us he needed to double his fee to supply us with our weekly social media reels. He had very kindly been doing us a favour at a reduced rate and it wasn't manageable for him anymore due to his workload. So, we did what any confident businesswomen would do: panicked.

We knew without even having to discuss it with one another that we couldn't afford his new rate and suddenly we were left without any videos to post on our social channels. First-world problems perhaps, but for a content business, a problem nonetheless.

Lauren and I went round in circles about what to do. I decided I wanted to try editing it myself so I began frantically googling "top video editing apps" – they all looked very complicated. I searched again: "top SIMPLE video editing apps". They all looked expensive. I tried a third time: "top SIMPLE video editing apps for free" – they didn't exist. I wasted an hour of my life I shall never get back but at least I know a bit more about video editing apps that I will never use. Not exactly working smart.

The awful reality of Instagram, or any social media, is that it stops for no one (this is not #selfcare), and we needed the reels for continuity and our sponsors, so time was of the essence.

It was somewhere between wondering how I was going to teach myself to video edit and worrying, that it dawned on me we were writing a chapter on work–life balance – oh, the irony – and, not only that, we were writing an entire book, which meant we categorically did not have the time or headspace for another job.

During a walk with my sister, she pointed out what was a priority and what was not and, unbeknownst to her, took me through the steps of this work smart practice. I can't believe I didn't do it for myself!

We decided the book and the podcast were priorities, and signing up for a course in video editing skills and paying £279 for an app I had no idea how to use, was not! I decided there and then to reread this chapter and take my own advice. We took the most practical approach and asked

James (our studio engineer) what he would charge to cut the reels for us. Needless to say, James now edits our social videos.

The moral of the story is: work smart!

WHAT DID WE LEARN?
Lauren
I learnt that over-preparing for this interview and working hard but not smart was really about my insecurities and feeling intimidated, rather than keeping my attention on prioritising my tasks. I really enjoyed this podcast guest's book and learning more about her, but I was doing myself a disservice by assuming that I needed to do a deep-dive into her entire life in order to achieve a good interview.

Nicole
Working hard and working smart are different. Taking a step back to ask myself where my priorities were was very helpful. I also learnt I have no interest in learning how to edit videos, because life is too short.

ASKING FOR HELP

Nobody achieves great things without the assistance and support of others. Listen to any Oscar acceptance speech or turn to the acknowledgements page of any book (including this one) and you will discover all the people who have helped along the way. No man is an island, and asking for help is a skill that is vital to achieving your goals.

Many of us feel shy about asking for help, or assume that we are bothering people. But if you are trying to solve a problem, or aiming to achieve a goal, having others to help you will increase your chances of success.

As social animals, human beings depend on one another to survive. In fact, research shows that helping others actually makes us feel good, but for many of us, the thought of asking for help might feel uncomfortable. It may make us feel anxious, dent our ego, undermine our confidence or make us question our abilities. So why is asking for help is so hard?

- **Fear**. Fear that we'll be turned down, rejected or laughed at. Even though these fears are usually unfounded, we are afraid to ask for help because it carries the risks of rejection and vulnerability.
- **Pride**. We don't want to be perceived as needy or come across as incompetent, so we work really hard to make sure people don't see us this way. You may also feel that people have their own worries to take care of, so yours aren't significant.
- **Discomfort**. Some people have a hard time with surrendering control to someone else. And some people have a *very* hard time with that (i.e. Lauren).

Fun Fact

Asking for help is a skill that we can all develop and that must be practised and perfected over time.

Unfun Fact

Too often, we wait for someone to notice our telepathic plea for help and then inevitably get frustrated when no one does.

Both Fun and Unfun Fact

In order to receive help, you have to ask for it.

SELF-CARE STEPS TO EMPOWER YOU TO EFFECTIVELY ASK FOR HELP

The *Who, What, Why* method.

Step 1: Who

Pick carefully *who* you ask for help. Are they reliable? Will they add to or take away your mental load? Are they likely to say yes? Not everyone will meet your needs.

Step 2: What

Communicate *what* you need clearly and concisely. There is no need to over-explain: simply describe what the task is and how the person you're asking can contribute. Try to be as specific as possible.

Step 3: Why

Express *why* you appreciate their help and *why* you are grateful.

An example of the steps in practice

- **WHO:** My mum.
- **WHAT:** I need some childcare help tomorrow, as I have an afternoon meeting and nobody to take care of Josh. Please can you pick him up from school at 3.30pm and look after him until 5pm, when I will pick him up from your house?
- **WHY:** I really appreciate your help as it allows me to get to a meeting. I know you'll do a great job of looking after him and I don't have to worry. Thank you so much.

EXTRA TIPS FOR THOSE STILL FEELING HESITANT

- **Don't apologise.** We all need help sometimes and it's nothing to be ashamed of. Apologising makes it seem like you're doing something wrong.

- **Asking for help is a sign of strength**. Lean into the discomfort.
- **If you still need convincing, let us ask you this**: if someone close to you asked for your help would you want to help them in some way and ease their stress? Thought so ...

OUR EXPERIENCE

Lauren

I'm very happy to be the person you can ask for help. But I do not ask for help and I do not want to. Being capable and independent is very important to me. On a deeper level, I think this stems from a fear of rejection that if I opened myself up I run the risk of my need not being met. I would then feel rejected and emotionally wounded. These feelings would be far worse than just sucking it up and trucking on by myself. I also like to always be in control, and I feel asking for help is a surrendering of control. The thought of anyone thinking of me as incapable or not coping is an edge for me, and I see it as a sign of weakness. Yet often, I also expect my husband to be psychic and offer help if I'm feeling overwhelmed. So, as you can imagine, this week made me feel uncomfortable and awkward.

The practice started with our 20th wedding anniversary party. I asked for help on the night by hiring my friend's son to help with the clearing up. Normally, I would just accept that I would be spending a lot of the evening carrying plates and glasses back and forth and not getting a chance to talk to anyone or enjoy the party fully. I decided to twist this round and not look at it as something that made me feel pathetic or incompetent, but instead as a positive that I could give specific instructions to someone trustworthy who could carry out tasks that freed me up. He did a great job, and he allowed me to enjoy the night and I gladly received the help. The other surprising outcome of this was that everyone was proud of me because they knew it was so unlike me to not take it all on myself.

Wednesday afternoons for me are a shitshow of hours lost in traffic, juggling the school run, football training and attempting to get dinner ready before getting back in the car again. I explained to my husband why Wednesday nights were tricky as he's not home to see what goes on, and asked him for help by picking our son up from football on his way home from work. He said, "Yes, of course. And I'll try to do it every week." Oh my God! Why didn't I ask him two years ago?

After feeling quite proud of myself, I was speaking to my friend Jodi who is a therapist. She asked what we were doing for our practice this week and when I told her we were asking for help she said, "Hmmm, I bet you're terrible at that." I agreed, then explained everything I had done. I expected praise, but instead she said, "What about asking for emotional help, Lauren? How are you at that?" I gave a retching sound. "Yeah", she said. "I thought as much. Because, you know asking for emotional help, that's the real work of asking for help?" I quickly and deliberately changed the subject.

Nicole
My husband often tells me to stop playing the martyr card, especially when I am moaning about my mental load. He says, "If you need help, just ask me and I will help you." It would be better if he could just read my mind but I was learning this was unrealistic.

The role I play is the "together one" or the "helper"; so asking for help goes against the grain. I suspected this was conditioning but, either way, I knew I had a lot of uncomfortable work to do.

I had six people coming for dinner and everyone asked what they could bring, I immediately gave my default answer of "Nothing!"

The day before the dinner I was on the phone to my close friend who was one of the guests. She was having a hard time with something and we had a vulnerable, raw conversation. At the end of the call, when she offered once again to bring a salad, I automatically said "no". I couldn't stand the thought of making her life any harder than it already was by giving her more "stuff" to do. She insisted, and I said "Okay, but I am only saying yes because it's 'asking for help' week." FYI: this is NOT how you ask for help.

The night of the dinner she walked in as planned with the salad and I took gratitude to a new level. It was as if she handed me a meal after being starved for a month. The thank yous went on and on – it was shameful and probably made her very uncomfortable. When my best friend (who knows me better than I know myself) noticed what was going on, she said, "What's with all the thanking? She's made a salad, she hasn't built you the Taj Mahal. Chill the fuck out!" I stopped immediately.

WHAT DID WE LEARN?
Lauren
I felt pleased with myself until Jodi made me think about my aversion to discussing my emotional needs.

I realised I'm just plain jealous of people who have the ability to say, "I am vulnerable", and who trust that they will receive the help they want and need. Whereas I ask for nothing for fear of not receiving it and, in return, receive none. I had to really prod that bruise, and it was painful.

The truth is, nobody thinks worse of you when you ask for help. It's an unused muscle that needs time to build.

Nicole
There is something in "asking for help" that challenges my idea of "taking up space", and finding comfort in that is part of my life's work. It's ironic considering what I do for a living, but perhaps that is no coincidence.

I have an assumption that people don't have time for me, and the role I have to play in their lives is the capable one who needs for nothing – which is not a truth, just an old story I made up. I am getting better at claiming my space in relationships where I feel safe, but with certain people I continue to find it very difficult. Asking for help feels like drinking poison – it's that uncomfortable for me.

Saying all that, I see the necessity of this practice.

TAKE-AWAY TIPS

Fika
The busier your day, the more important it is that you make time for fika.

Work smart
Decide what needs prioritising for the day, the hour, or even that minute – and execute *that* task. Do not do anything that isn't urgent or could be done at another time.

Asking for help
This is not a sign of weakness, it is a sign of being human. Asking for help and receiving it is the key to success. Just make sure you ask the right people.

READER CHALLENGES

Lauren's challenge
The next time that somebody offers to help you, say "yes". Be confident and comfortable that it gives them pleasure to help you and that you deserve to be helped.

Nicole's challenge
Pick one person who you trust and ask them for the help you need.

Bonus challenge
Say "no" to any meetings that waste your time and don't serve you.

Conclusion

Now that you've come to the end of the book and have delved into the practices, we invite you to revisit the Wellness Wheel you first created in the Introduction.

Return to the Wellness Questions on pages 16 and 17, and answer these again. Fill in your scores on the blank wheel on page 226 and compare this with your wheel on page 19. Have your scores in each category changed at all?

Check in with yourself: what has improved and how do you feel now versus when you started reading the book?

Self-improvement is a lifelong task. It would be unrealistic to expect magic to be worked overnight. Different stages of your life will require different elements of self-care, as at times you may not have the space for some things, while others need to be prioritised.

OUR LEARNINGS

As we have asked you to assess your progress through reading this book, we thought it only fair we reflect on what we have learnt too!

Lauren

What I have learnt from four years of focusing on self-care (and writing a book on it) is that I am still evolving and changing as I come into the middle stage of my life – as we all are. I have discovered tools to support me in my natural propensity to be conflict-avoidant. Although I still find it an edge, I am better at having difficult conversations and setting boundaries. I am also using my "no" more in order to say "yes" to the things and the people that add to my life.

I have learnt that asking for what I want is imperative, as nobody is sitting around waiting to give me opportunities; it's something I have to reach out for myself. I have also cut back on my tendency to people-please. What other people think of me is none of my business, and I cannot live my life on somebody else's terms and conditions, for fear of being disliked. It is never too late to address things about myself that I have always held to be true, and it's never too late to change them and the narrative I have created for myself.

My hope is that if you picked up this book with a desire to move from a place of inertia, just one singular practice may have inspired you to take action and has been the catalyst you needed to create change.

If you have a problem that is holding you back or preventing you from living fully, and you can see a way to help yourself by trying out a practice that resonates with you, try it! You have nothing to lose. If, after following it through, you can see some improvement, then you may feel encouraged to try another ... and then it becomes a positive wheel set in motion.

Nicole

The practices in this book have been life changing for me. I no longer take a passive approach in my own life, and when the world tells me that I should, I now have the tools to fight against it. The narrative that, as a woman, I should remain small, silent and unassuming simply no longer work for me. My life is mine and I choose to live it my way.

I choose to say "no" to things that don't serve me and "yes" to the things that do. I choose to ask for what I want – because it is imperative to creating it – and to ask for help along the way. I choose to celebrate my achievements, listen to my own opinion, respect myself and remove toxic behaviour. I have cultivated my relationships to only surround myself with people who accept and support me just as I am – flaws and all – because that is the true meaning of friendship. Perhaps the hardest lesson for me has been how to love and accept my body for all that it does, and this remains a work in progress.

The best part of all this learning is that I choose not to apologise for any of it. This work brings empowerment to live life on your own terms; being able to pass it onto you, in the hope that it brings your own transformation, fills me with abundant humility.

FIND YOUR VERSION OF SELF-CARE

Please remember that self-care is here to nourish you to feel better and make your life richer. If it creates anything but that, it simply isn't self-care. Practise it in your own time and on your own terms and do it solely for you.

We hope that reading this book has inspired you to take the time and allow space for what may be needed in your life. We also hope that your self-care toolbox is full – or on its way to being there.

Self-care is a lifelong exciting journey, and one that supports you wherever you may be. As we grow, so must the way we look after ourselves. Perhaps in time, Nicole will find enjoyment in taking time to rest and Lauren will learn to appreciate high-impact activity. The truth is, it doesn't matter. All that matters is that we are listening to our minds, bodies and spirits and giving them what they need – this is the truest act of self-love and respect.

YOUR WELLNESS WHEEL

Revisit the questions in the Introduction and fill out the wheel below. How does it compare to your wheel on page 19?

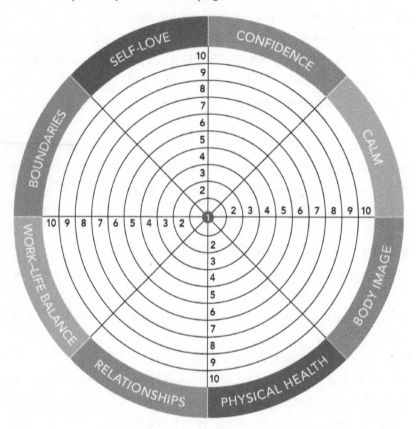

References

Boogaard, K (2023). Finding Your Work-Life Balance as a Remote Employee. *Fingerprint For Success.* www.fingerprintforsuccess.com/blog/work-life-balance-stats

Ferrari, JR and Roster, CA (2018). Delaying Disposing: Examining the Relationship between Procrastination and Clutter across Generations. *Curr Psychol. 37,* 426–431. https://doi.org/10.1007/s12144-017-9679-4

Fredrickson, BL and Losada, MF (2005). Positive affect and the complex dynamics of human flourishing. *The American Psychologist. 60(7),* 678–686. https://doi.org/10.1037/0003-066X.60.7.678

Hamasaki, H (2020). Effects of Diaphragmatic Breathing on Health: A Narrative Review. *Medicines (Basel). Oct 15;7(10),* 65. https://doi.org/10.3390/medicines7100065

Kerai, A (2023). Cell Phone Usage Statistics: Mornings Are for Notifications. *Reviews.org.* www.reviews.org/mobile/cell-phone-addiction/#:~:text=So%20scroll%20down%20and%20let%27s,leaving%20their%20phone%20at%20home

Mental Health UK (2023). What is anxiety disorder? mentalhealth-uk.org/help-and-information/conditions/anxiety-disorders/what-is-anxiety/

Mind (2023). Mental Health Facts and Statistics. www.mind.org.uk/information-support/types-of-mental-health-problems/statistics-and-facts-about-mental-health/how-common-are-mental-health-problems/#:~:text=In%20any%20given%20week%20in%20England%20%5B2%5D%3A,PTSD)%3A%204%20in%20100%20people

Misra, S, Cheng, L, Genevie, J and Yuan, M (2016). The iPhone Effect: The Quality of In-Person Social Interactions in the Presence of Mobile Devices. *Environment and Behavior. 48(2),* 275–298. https://doi.org/10.1177/0013916514539755

Monroy, M and Keltner, D (2023). Awe as a Pathway to Mental and Physical Health. *Perspect Psychol Sci. 18(2),* 309–320. https://doi.org/10.1177/17456916221094856

National Academies of Sciences, Engineering, and Medicine (2020). Social Isolation and Loneliness in Older Adults: Opportunities for the Health Care System. *Washington, DC: The National Academies Press.* https://doi.org/10.17226/25663

O'Brien, KR (2014). Just Saying "No": An Examination of Gender Differences in the Ability to Decline Requests in the Workplace. *Diss, Rice University.* https://hdl.handle.net/1911/77421

Oberlo (2023). How Much Is the Beauty Industry Worth? (2018–2028). www.oberlo.com/statistics/how-much-is-the-beauty-industry-worth

Royal Society of Public Health and Youth Health Movement (2017). #StatusOfMind: Social Media and Young People's Mental Health and Wellbeing. *RSPH, London.* https://www.rsph.org.uk/uploads/assets/uploaded/62be270a-a55f-4719-ad668c2ec7a74c2a.pdf

Shevchuk, NA (2008). Adapted cold shower as a potential treatment for depression. *Med Hypotheses. 70(5),* 995–1001. https://doi.org/10.1016/j.mehy.2007.04.052

Small, DA, Gelfand, M, Babcock, L and Gettman, H (2007). Who goes to the bargaining table? The influence of gender and framing on the initiation of negotiation. *Journal of Personality and Social Psychology. 93(4),* 600–613. https://doi.org/10.1037/0022-3514.93.4.600

Suni, E and Dimitriu, A (2023). What Is "Revenge Bedtime Procrastination"? *Sleep Foundation.* www.sleepfoundation.org/sleep-hygiene/revenge-bedtime-procrastination#references-81460

Tyng, CM, Amin, HU, Saad, MNM and Malik, AS (2017). The Influences of Emotion on Learning and Memory. *Front Psychol. Aug 24;8,* 1454. https://doi.org/10.3389/fpsyg.2017.01454

West, K (2018). Naked and Unashamed: Investigations and Applications of the Effects of Naturist Activities on Body Image, Self-Esteem, and Life Satisfaction. *J Happiness Stud. 19,* 677–697. https://doi.org/10.1007/s10902-017-9846-1

Further Resources

Below are some places you can access help and support, organised by the chapter themes we use in the book.

BOUNDARIES
Doyle, Glennon, *Untamed: Stop Pleasing, Start Living* (Vermilion, 2020)

SELF LOVE
Self-esteem Self-help Guide: a step-by-step guide using CBT to improve self-esteem. https://www.nhsinform.scot/illnesses-and-conditions/mental-health/mental-health-self-help-guides/self-esteem-self-help-guide/

Raising Low Self-Esteem: NHS article. https://www.nhs.uk/mental-health/self-help/tips-and-support/raise-low-self-esteem/

CONFIDENCE
British Association for Counsellors and Psychotherapists: Find an expert trained in talking therapy. bacp.co.uk

CALM
Anxiety UK: A user-led organisation supporting anyone with anxiety, phobias, panic attacks or other anxiety disorders. www.anxietyuk.org.uk

CALM: The Campaign Against Living Miserably (CALM) is leading a movement against suicide.www.thecalmzone.net (webchat: 5pm–midnight)

Samaritans: Phoneline open 24/7 for anyone who needs to talk. You can visit some Samaritans branches in person. www.samaritans.org. Tel: 116 123 (freephone); Email: jo@samaritans.org; Freepost: SAMARITANS LETTERS

Social Anxiety UK: A web-based organisation supporting those with social anxiety disorder; they offer forums, a chat room and information. www.social-anxiety.org.uk

OCD-UK: Provides information, advice and support on obsessive compulsive disorder (OCD) and related disorders, such as body dysmorphic disorder (BDD), skin-picking and hair pulling. www.ocduk.org

BODY IMAGE

Beat: The UK's Eating Disorder Charity has advisors who can talk to you about the different types of eating disorders, and provide information about recovery and the support available to you. www.beateatingdisorders.org.uk. Adult Helpline: 0808 801 0677; Adult email: help@beateatingdisorders.org.uk; Youthline: 0808 801 0711; Youth email: fyp@beateatingdisorders.org.uk

PHYSICAL HEALTH

Couch to 5K: Information available at the web address. Also download the app for free. www.nhs.uk/live-well/exercise/running-and-aerobic-exercises/get-running-with-couch-to-5k/

The Sleep Charity: A national charity empowering the nation to sleep better. thesleepcharity.co.uk

The National Sleep Helpline: A confidential service for adults and children with sleep problems. 03303530541

The British Nutrition Foundation: Impartial, evidence-based information, resources and training on food and nutrition. nutrition.org.uk

Eat Well: Food guidelines, food labels, 5 A Day, food types and digestive health. www.nhs.uk/live-well/eat-well

ZOE Science & Nutrition Podcast: Discover the latest health, nutrition and gut health research and get practical advice.

RELATIONSHIPS
Relate: A UK-based charity that offers confidential and professional counselling and support for couples and families. www.relate.org.uk

WORK-LIFE BALANCE
Pregnant Then Screwed: A charity dedicated to ending the workplace motherhood penalty, supporting tens of thousands of women each year, and successfully campaigning for change. www. pregnantthenscrewcom

Health and Safety Executive (HSE): Information and guidance on health and safety law in the workplace. hse.gov.uk

Mind Tools: Tips and articles on personal effectiveness, management and leadership. mindtools.com

Citizens Advice: There to advise on legal, debt, consumer, housing and other problems in the UK. www.citizensadvice.org.uk/work/

Stress Management Society: Information about stress and tips on how to cope. stress.org.uk

Women Returners: Provides career advice for women returning to work after time out. www.womenreturners.com

Acknowledgements

Many thanks to:

Our agent Hattie Grunewald at The Blair Partnership. Your support and guidance has been invaluable as we navigated our way through writing our first book. This book wouldn't be what it is without you. Our editors Beth Bishop and Matt Tomlinson for your keen eyes and helpful direction. Jenny Phillips for your faith and introduction. The team at Welbeck – Isabelle Wilson, Kirsty Capes, Margarida Mendez-Ribeiro – thank you for helping us bring this book to life. Jo Lal for championing our cause and understanding our vision.

James Alexander (love you James) and Launchpod studios for tolerating the madness every Monday morning, for your infectious energy and all your creative brainstorming sessions. Our manager Lydia Rodford at DN Talent for your boundless enthusiasm. Andy and the team at Adelicious for coming along at just the right time and for your ongoing support.

Our husbands Adam and Ollie. Thank you for your patience, support and love. For turning a blind eye to every weird item that appears in the house, for allowing us to test some of this stuff out on you and for being our cheerleaders. For not being jealous of us spending vastly more time with each other than with you and for finding your own friendship with one another which makes life more fun.

Our children Max, Zak, Daisy, Lilyrose and Josh: thank you for every eye roll – sorry (not sorry) for being on TikTok and talking about vaginas – your embarrassment keeps us humble. You all inspire us to be the best women and mums that we can be.

Our self-care pair – the best dogs in the whole world, Barker and Miley – for being so happy together and allowing us to write in peace.

Our parents Tony, Benita, Jackie and Russ for being in our corner, for being our very first listeners and for metaphorically sitting in the front row giving us the thumbs up.

From Nicole: My sister Lisa for being my constant companion, my spiritual ally and the truest person in my life. I couldn't and wouldn't do life without you. You are my self-care!

Our wider families and friends: KP for the intro, Jon S for shoving us in the right direction, SHG and especially Charlotte Simpson for introducing us – without you we would never have found each other.

All the wonderful experts and guests who have enriched the podcast and shared their wisdom with us and our listeners. Thank you for being a part of the club.

Lastly, and probably most importantly, a heartfelt thank you to all our loyal and lovely "clubbers". We feel it a huge privilege to be the friends in your ears every week. Thank you for listening, supporting and encouraging us to continue to debunk the wellness world and bring true self-care to all. This book is for you.